Horizons

Preschool

Book 1

Lessons 1-90

Author:

Alan Christopherson

Graphic Design:

Jennifer Davis

Illustration:

Keith Piccolo

Original Interlock Curriculum by
Rebecca L. Avery

 **AOP**

804 N. 2nd Ave. E.   Rock Rapids, IA 51246-1759   800-622-3070   www.aop.com

Horizons Preschool, Book 1

A Horizons Preschool Student Book should be purchased for each student, whether in the Christian School classroom or in the Homeschool. In the classroom setting, always order one extra for the teacher so that you have copies of everything to reference. Students will take home the pages of the Student Book throughout the year.

You may use whatever Bible version your family studies. The Horizons Preschool uses the KJV King James Version and the NIV New International Version of the Bible. Scripture is taken from the HOLY BIBLE, NEW INTERNATIONAL VERSION® Copyright ©1973, 1978, 1984 by International Bible Society. Used by permission of Zondervan. All rights reserved.

Printed in the United States of America

ISBN 978-0-7403-1447-6

Trace the letters A and a with your finger. Can you see the letters Aa at the beginning of the words apple, armadillo, ax, ant, ape, and alligator?

Apple
apple

Armadillo
armadillo

Ape
ape

Ax
ax

Ant
ant

Ark
ark

Alligator
alligator

1

Lesson 1 Math

Identify the pictures and count the number in each group. Trace the lines to match the ones that are the same.

Cut out the numbers. Count each group and paste the correct number in the square.

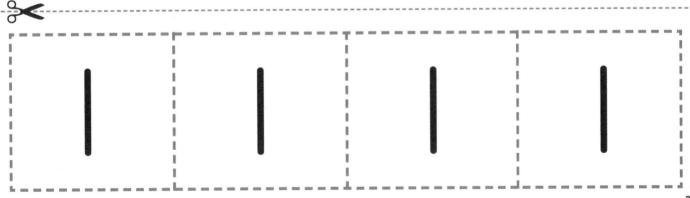

3

Find the path in the maze from the uppercase letter A to the lowercase letter a.

Letter Aa

Apple
apple

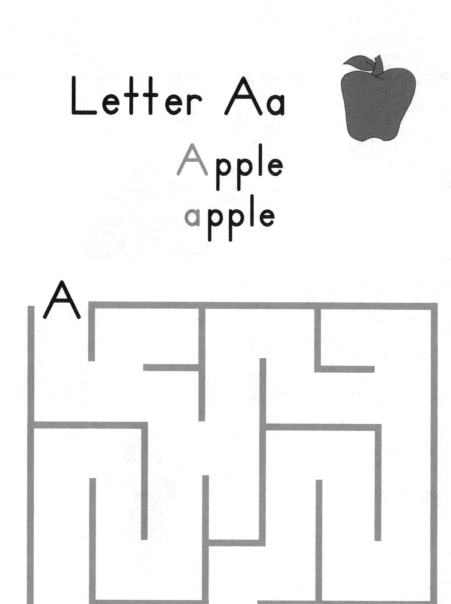

Cut out the items and glue them on a sheet of white construction paper as illustrated by the sample. Draw in the arms and face for the 1 lady. Glue glitter on the lamp flame. Glue toothpicks and yarn on the drawing to make the broom.

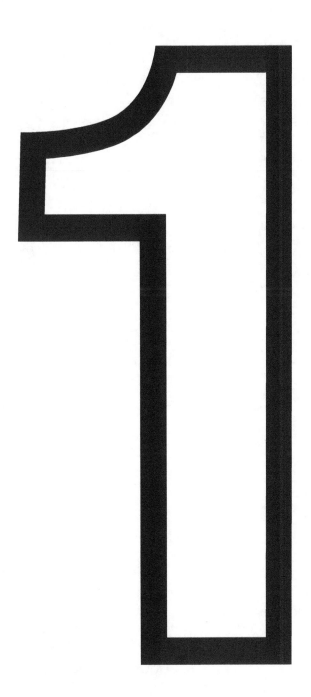

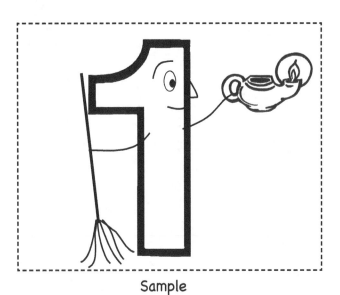

Sample

Color the things that God and Jesus created.

Use your scissors to cut them out.

Paste them on a piece of heavy paper.

Students: With the help of your parent, draw a simple picture of the place where you live. Bring it back to school tomorrow.

Parents: Let the child have fun. Don't expect perfection. Be sure that the homework is returned to class tomorrow.

10

Trace the triangle with a red, blue, or green crayon. You may color the triangle.

triangle

Lesson 3 Math

Count each group. Circle the correct number under each picture.

Color the picture of Heaven.

Trace the letters A and a with your finger. Can you see the letters Aa at the beginning of the words anteater, antelope, armadillo, agouti, and addax?

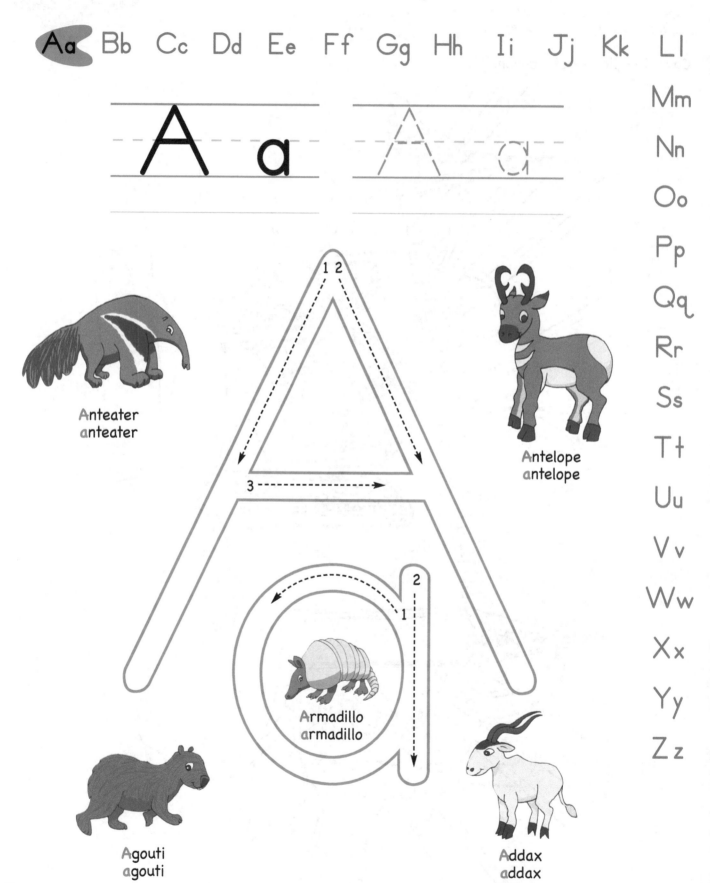

Aa Bb Cc Dd Ee Ff Gg Hh Ii Jj Kk Ll
Mm Nn Oo Pp Qq Rr Ss Tt Uu Vv Ww Xx Yy Zz

Anteater
anteater

Antelope
antelope

Armadillo
armadillo

Agouti
agouti

Addax
addax

Trace and color the triangles red and then cut them out.

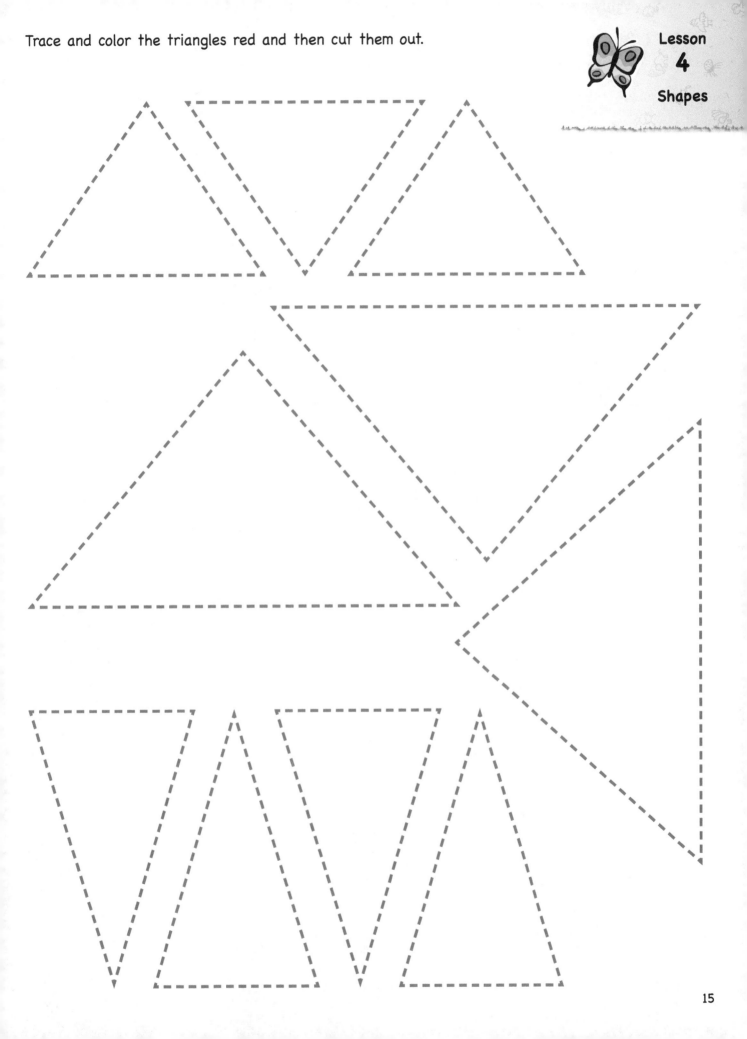

Count each group. Trace the lines to the correct number.

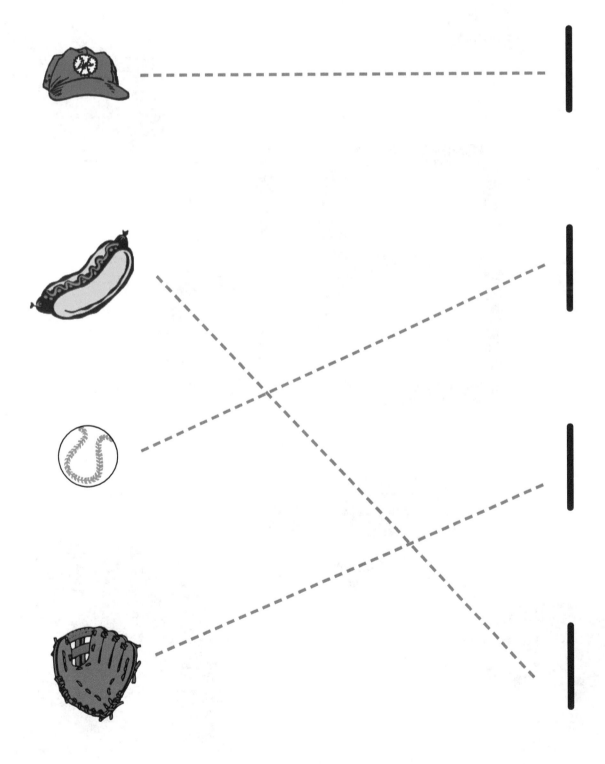

Lesson 5 Phonics

Trace the letters B and b with your finger. Can you see the letters Bb at the beginning of the words bee, bat, ball, beaver, badger, and bear?

Bee
bee

Bat
bat

Ball
ball

Beaver
beaver

Badger
badger

Bear
bear

Trace and color the triangles blue and then cut them out.

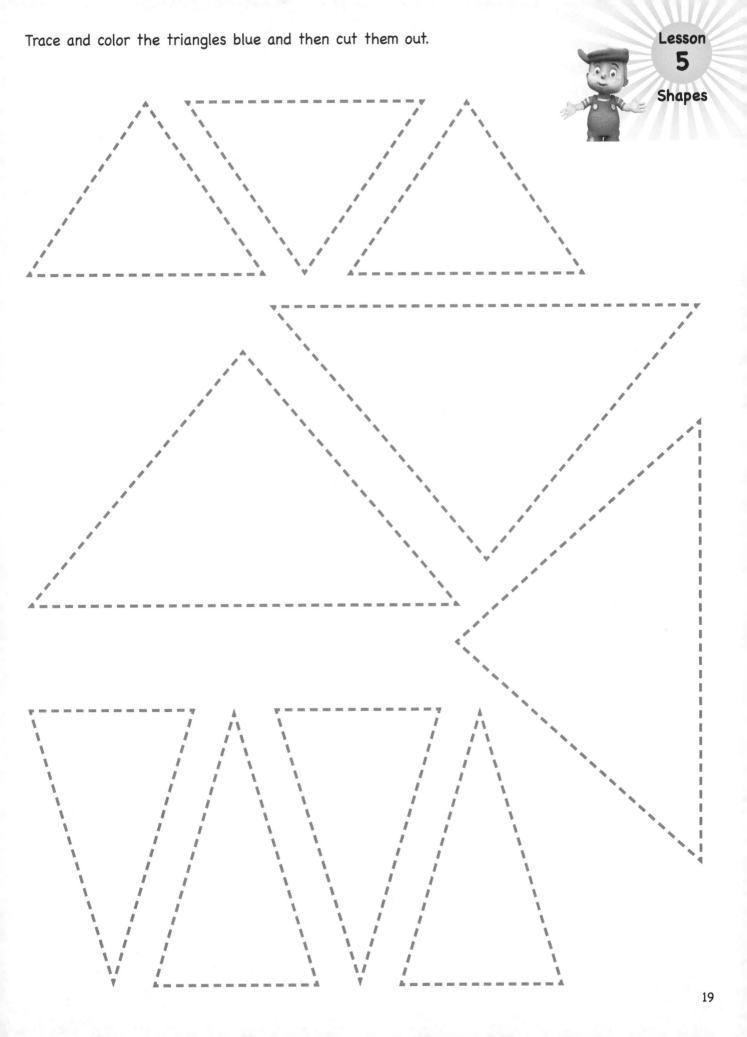

Use your finger to trace the large number 1. Count the animals and use a pencil to trace the numbers on the lines.

 1   2   3   4   5   6   7   8   9   10   11   12

Lesson 6 Math

Count each group. Trace the lines to match the ones that have the same number.

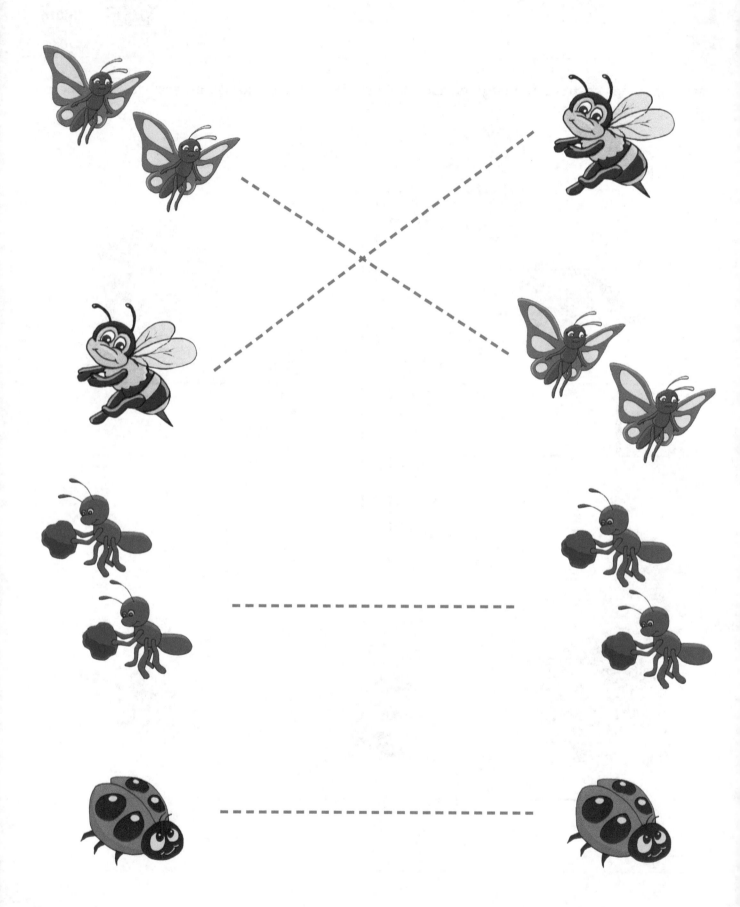

Trace and color the triangles green and then cut them out.

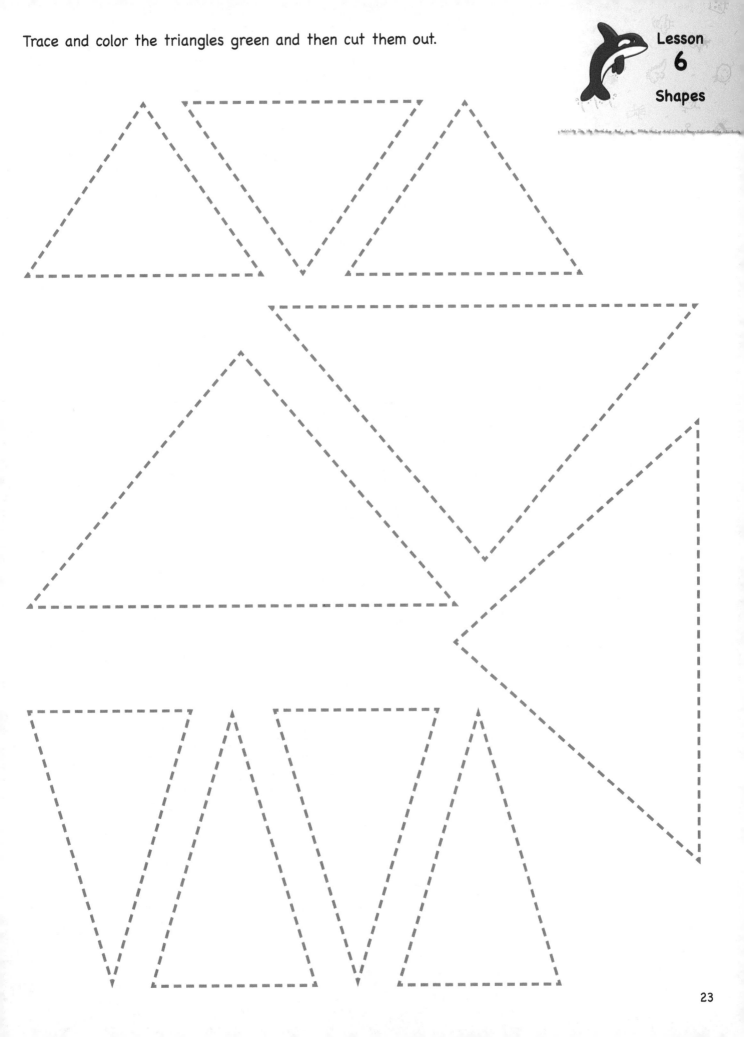

Trace the letters B and b with your finger. Can you see the letters Bb at the beginning of the words buffalo, bongo, butterfly, and bee?

Aa **Bb** Cc Dd Ee Ff Gg Hh Ii Jj Kk Ll
Mm
Nn
Oo
Pp
Qq
Rr
Ss
Tt
Uu
Vv
Ww
Xx
Yy
Zz

B b   B b

1 2

Buffalo
buffalo

3

Butterfly
butterfly

1

Bongo
bongo

2

Bee
bee

25

Lesson 7 Homework

Students: With your parents' help, do a chore tonight. Help with dinner, help with the dishes, fold some laundry... do something to help your parents. Then draw a picture of yourself doing the chore. Bring it back to class tomorrow.

Parents: Your student should be learning to do regular chores. This might be a good time to start a daily chore, one that the student is capable of doing alone.

Cut out the numbers. Count each group and paste the correct number in the box.

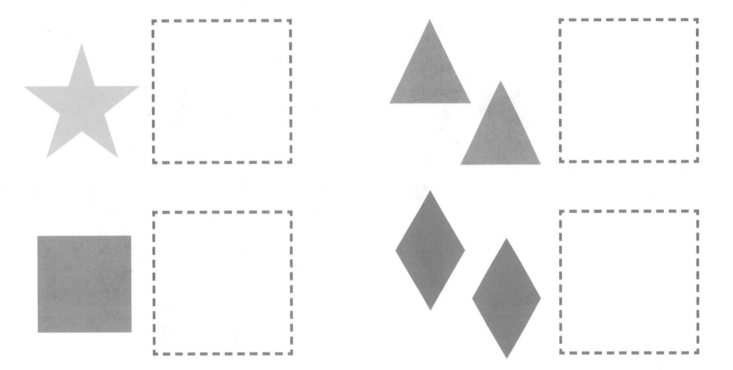

✂ -

| 1 | 2 | 1 | 2 |

Lesson 7 Shapes

Color, cut out, and paste the triangles on the hats.

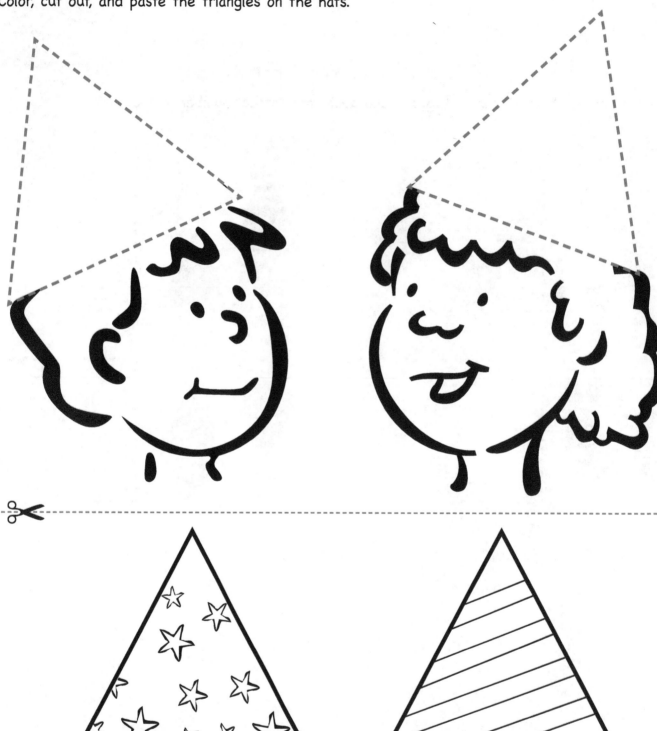

Cut out the items and glue them on a sheet of white construction paper as illustrated by the sample. Draw in the arms and faces for the 2 boys. Draw a tent in the background and sand under the numbers.

Sample

29

Trace the letters C and c with your finger. Can you see the letters Cc at the beginning of the words coyote, crab, cat, caterpillar, and camel?

Coyote
coyote

Crab
crab

Cat
cat

Caterpillar
caterpillar

Camel
camel

31

Lesson 8 Math

Count the animals in each group. Trace the line to the correct number.

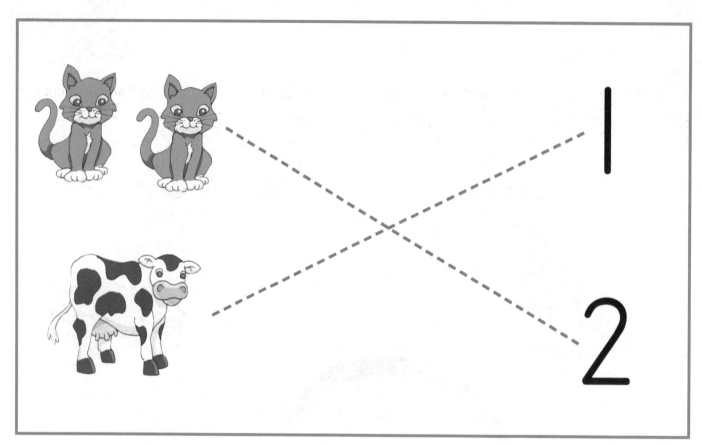

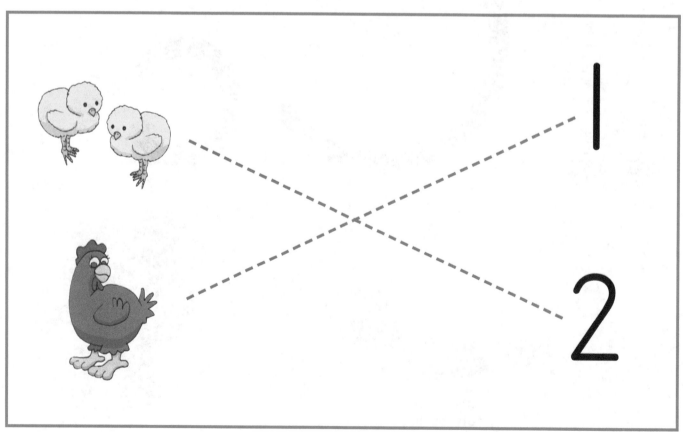

Trace the triangles. There are _____ triangles. Color the picture.

Lesson 8 Homework

Students: This project will help you to do your chores at home. Get a piece of paper, preferably card stock. Fold the paper in half. Lay your hand on the paper, with the heel of your hand against the fold. Have your parent help you trace around your hand. Then cut out the hand, but do not cut the fold. When the paper is opened, it will make two hands hooked together, side by side. Keep this chore card at home.

Parents: Help your child draw and cut out their hand card. Help them write: I HELP on the outside of the hands. Every time the child does a chore, they get a sticker inside the card. Ten stickers earn a special treat. We suggest you keep the treat small. Trips to the park or a visit to a friend make great treats.

Trace the letters C and c with your finger. Can you see the letters Cc at the beginning of the words cow, crow, chick, and clam?

Aa Bb **Cc** Dd Ee Ff Gg Hh Ii Jj Kk Ll

C c   C c

Mm
Nn
Oo
Pp
Qq
Rr
Ss
Tt
Uu
Vv
Ww
Xx
Yy
Zz

1

Cow
cow

Crow
crow

Chick
chick

Clam
clam

Lesson 9 Math & Shapes

Count each group and circle the correct number.

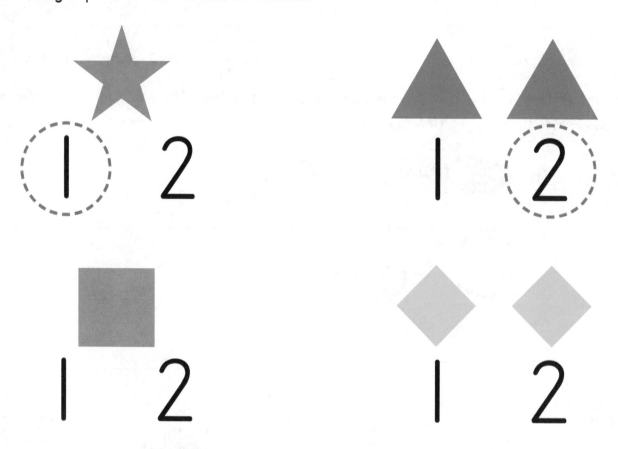

Trace the triangles. Color the big triangle red. Color the small triangle blue.

Draw a line between the items that go together. Use the dotted lines as your guide.

Draw a red X on Aa. Draw a blue triangle around Bb. Draw a green X on Cc.

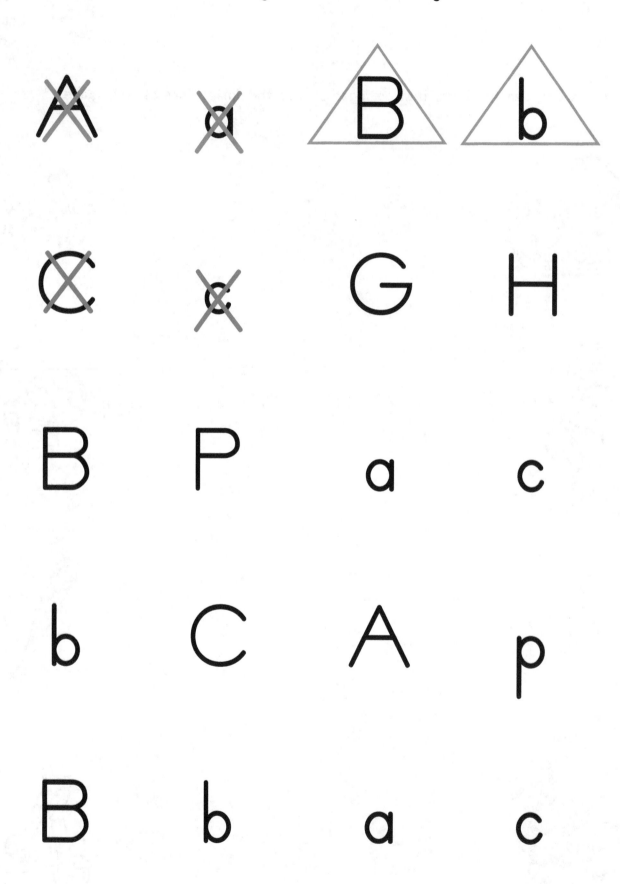

Use your finger to trace the large number 2. Count the animals and use a pencil to trace the numbers on the lines.

 1 2 3 4 5 6 7 8 9 10 11 12

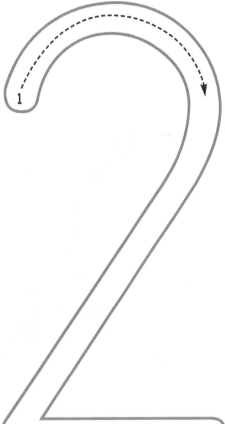

2 2

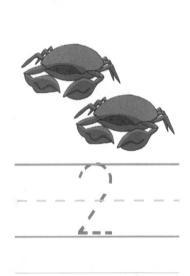

2

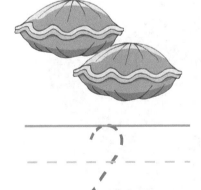

2

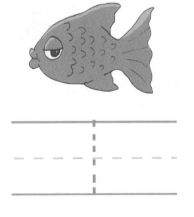

1

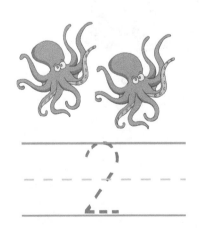

2

Trace the letters D and d with your finger. Can you see the letters Dd at the beginning of the words deer, dolphin, dog, dragonfly, and dinosaur?

Deer
deer

Dolphin
dolphin

Dog
dog

Dragonfly
dragonfly

Dinosaur
dinosaur

Count each group. Trace the line to the group that matches.

Lesson 11 Shapes

Trace the circle. You may color the circle.

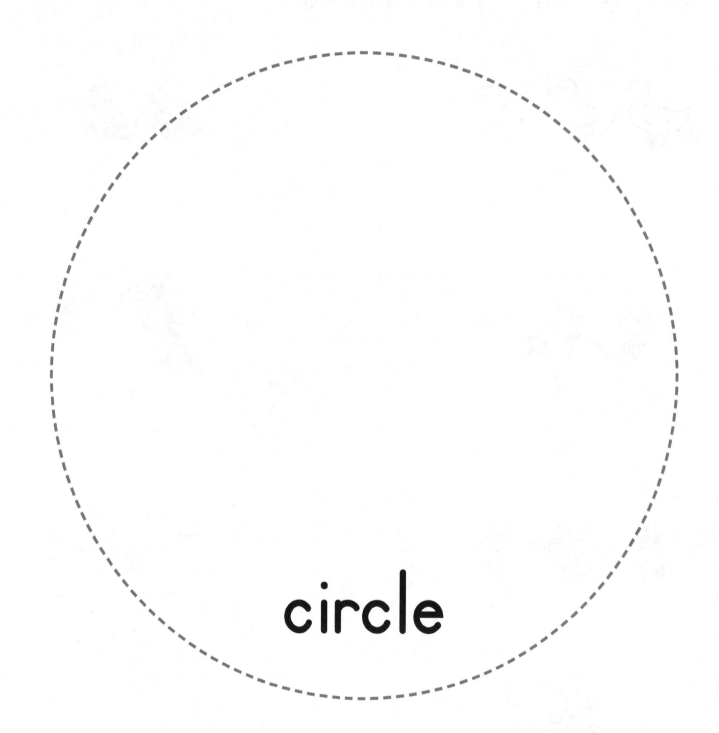

circle

Color and cut out the candle pieces. Glue the holder and candle to construction paper as illustrated by the sample. Glue the flame on the candle after you have said your memory verse.

Sample

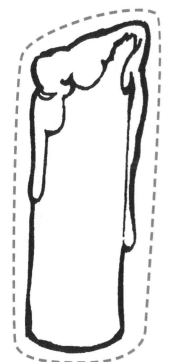

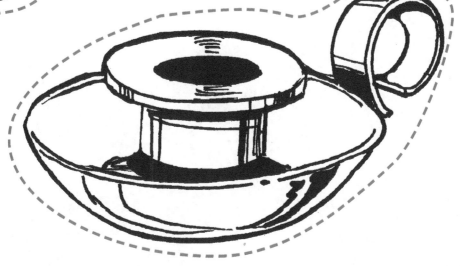

Count each group. Trace the lines to the number for each group.

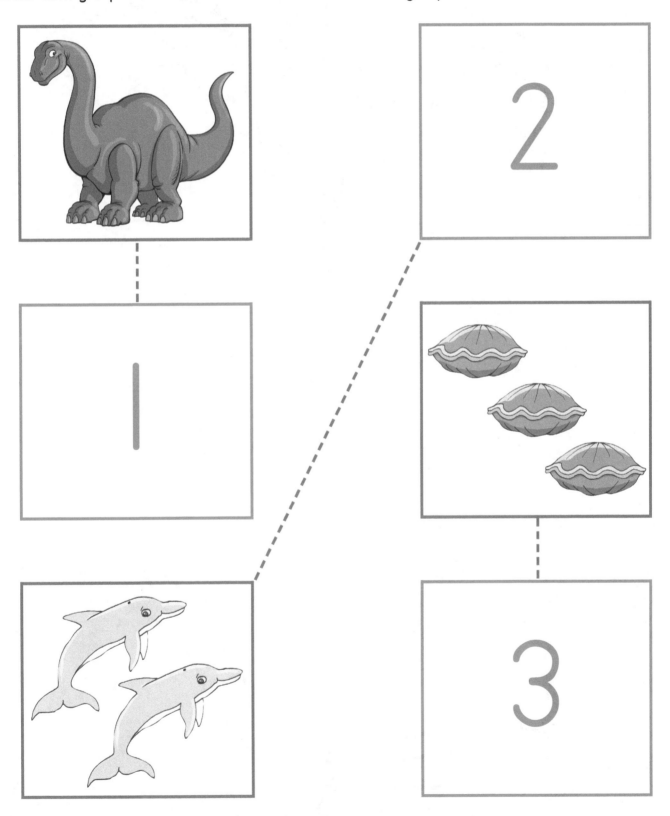

Find the numbers 1, 2, and 3 on the drawing. Connect the dots to make the picture.
You may color the flower.

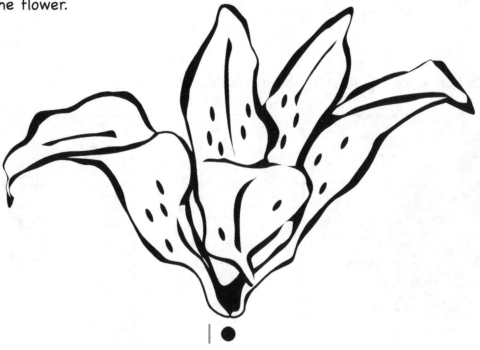

1 ●

2 ●

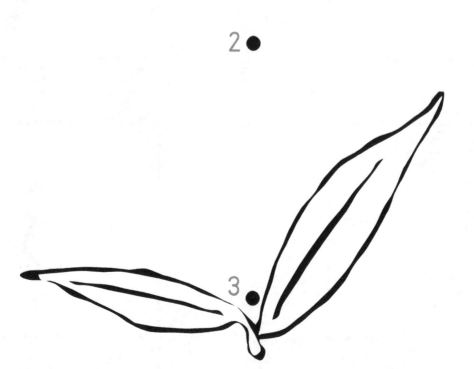

3 ●

Count the circles. Color, cut, and paste the circles to make the flowers.

✂ -

Students: Go outside tonight with a parent when it is dark. Stand and listen. Look around. What is different at night? Think about every sense: seeing, hearing, feeling, smelling, tasting. What do you see? What do you hear? Smell? Feel? Draw some things you observed on this page and return it to your class tomorrow.

Parents: Take your child outside to observe the nighttime. Help them to notice anything and everything that is different at night. Help them remember the differences.

Cut out the items on the worksheet and glue them to construction paper as illustrated by the sample. Draw in the arms, legs, and face for the 3 king. Glue glitter and spice to the 3 as indicated and drop some perfume as indicated.

Sample

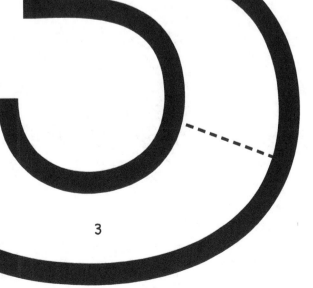

1

Glue glitter to section 1.

2

Drop perfume on section 2.

Glue spice to section 3.

3

Name

Count the flowers. Color the pictures. Cut out the flowers and glue them to the plant. Trace the number 3 on the pot.

Count each group. Draw a circle around the number for each group.

1	2	3

1	2	3

1	2	3

1	2	3

1	2	3

1	2	3

1	2	3

1	2	3

Lesson 13c Math

Draw a circle around the item in each row that is different.

Trace the circles in the picture. There are _____ circles. Color the picture.

Lesson 14 Phonics

Trace the letters D and d with your finger. Can you see the letters Dd at the beginning of the words donkey, duck, dragonfly, dog, and dinosaur?

Aa Bb Cc Dd Ee Ff Gg Hh Ii Jj Kk Ll

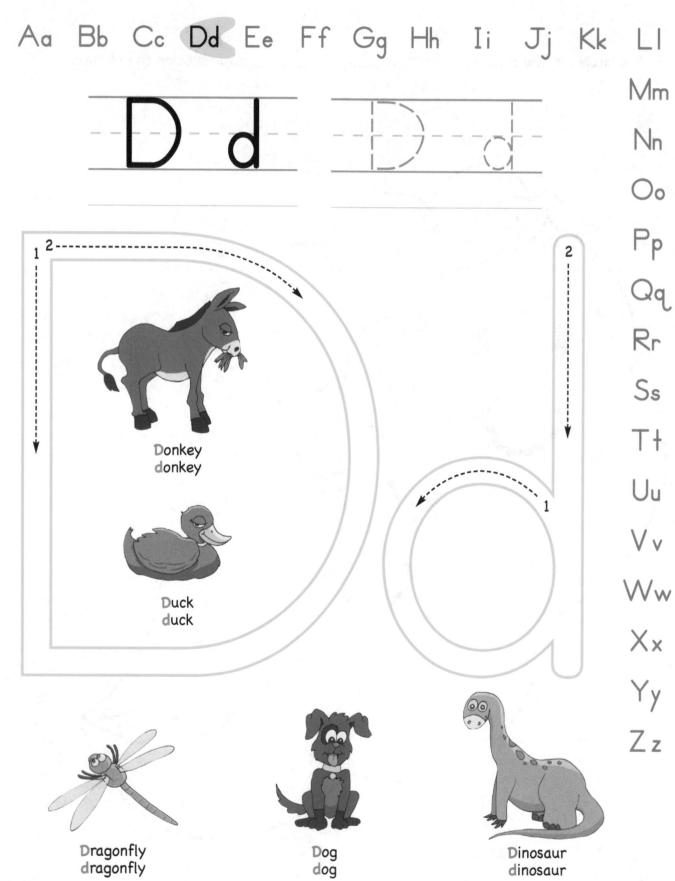

Mm
Nn
Oo
Pp
Qq
Rr
Ss
Tt
Uu
Vv
Ww
Xx
Yy
Zz

Donkey
donkey

Duck
duck

Dragonfly
dragonfly

Dog
dog

Dinosaur
dinosaur

Count each group. Trace the line to the number for each group.

Lesson 14b Math

Find the numbers 1, 2, and 3 on the drawing. Connect the dots to make the picture. You may color the picture.

1 •

• 3

2 •

Name

○ ○   ○ ○   ○ ○   ○ ○   ○ ○   ○ ○   ○ ○

○ ○   ○ ○   ○ ○   ○ ○   ○ ○   ○ ○   ○ ○

○ ○   ○ ○   ○ ○   ○ ○   ○ ○   ○ ○   ○ ○

Students: Look below to see what Braille looks like. Tomorrow in school you will be learning more about Braille. Pick out the letters that are in your name. Bring this sheet back to class tomorrow.

Parents: As the students pick out the letters that are in their name, help them fill in the dots above that are below their name. They will be using this guide to make their names in Braille tomorrow.

A   B   C   D   E   F   G

H   I   J   K   L   M   N

O   P   Q   R   S   T   U

V   W   X   Y   Z

Trace the letters E and e with your finger. Can you see the letters Ee at the beginning of the words eraser, eight, earth, elephant, and eagle?

Eraser
eraser

Earth
earth

Eight
eight

Elephant
elephant

Eagle
eagle

Lesson 15 Math

Use your finger to trace the large number 3. Count the animals and use a pencil to trace the numbers on the lines.

1 2 3 4 5 6 7 8 9 10 11 12

3

Count each group. Draw a line to the group that matches.

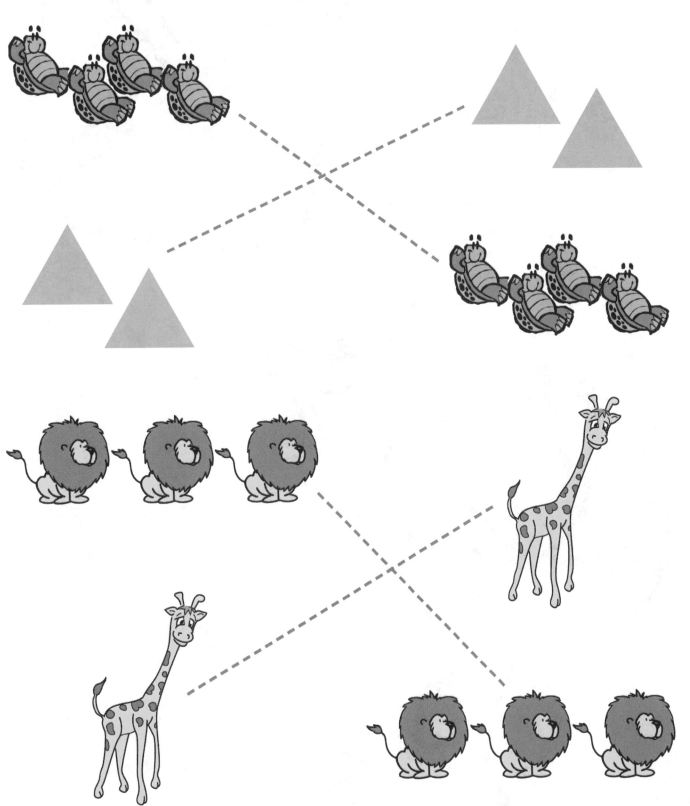

65

Lesson 16 Shapes

Count the triangles in the picture. Circle the number on the bottom of the page.
Color the picture.

2   3   4

Draw a line from the farm animal to its shadow.

Lesson 17 Phonics

Trace the letters E and e with your finger. Can you see the letters Ee at the beginning of the words ermine, egret, elk, emu, and earthworm?

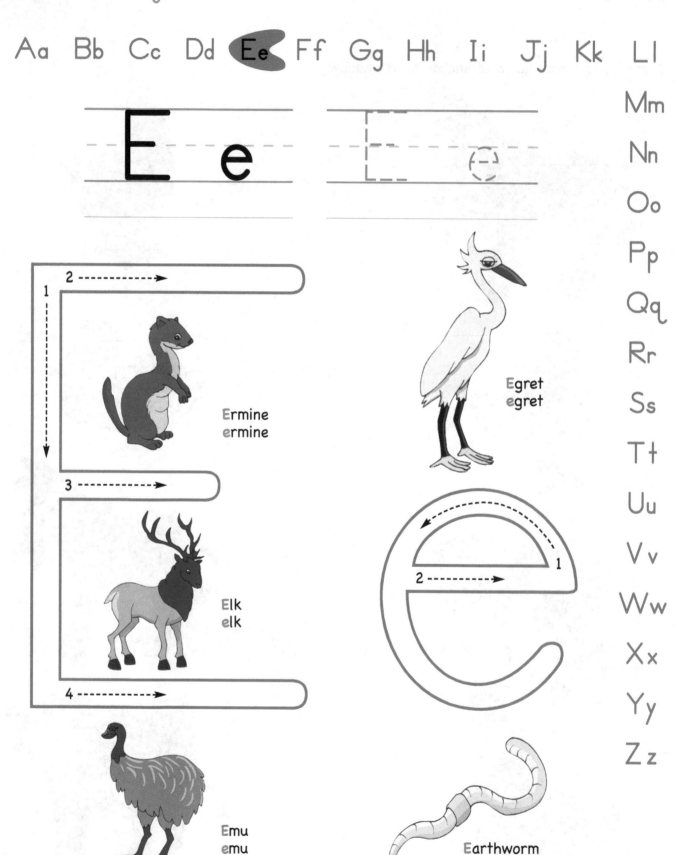

Aa Bb Cc Dd Ee Ff Gg Hh Ii Jj Kk Ll
Mm Nn Oo Pp Qq Rr Ss Tt Uu Vv Ww Xx Yy Zz

Ermine
ermine

Egret
egret

Elk
elk

Emu
emu

Earthworm
earthworm

Say the **Baa, Baa, Black Sheep** rhyme. Count the bags of wool. Trace the missing number(s) in each row as you count 1, 2, 3.

Baa, Baa, Black Sheep
Baa, baa, black sheep, have you any wool?
Yes sir, yes sir, three bags full!
One for my master, one for my dame and one
for the little boy who lives down the lane.

1	2	3
1	2	3
1	2	3
1	2	3
1	2	3
1	2	3
1	2	3
1	2	3

69

Lesson 17b Math

Trace the numbers. Count each group. Trace the line from the group to the number.

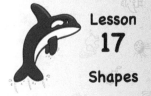
Color the large circles blue and the small circles red. Use the other colors studied so far, green, black, white, and yellow to color the rest of the picture.

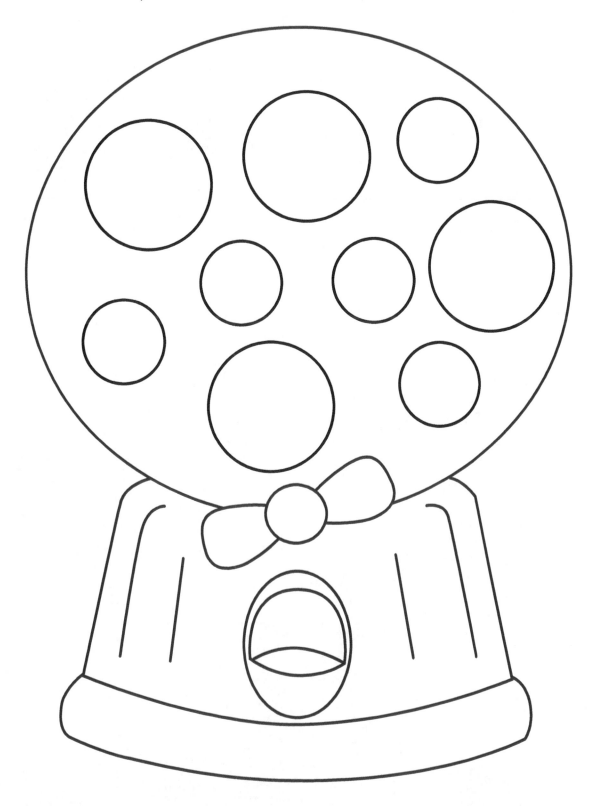

Cut out the items on the worksheet and glue them to construction paper as illustrated by the sample. Draw in the arms, legs, and face for the 4 fisherman. Draw in the rest of the picture.

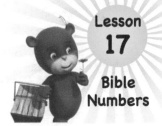

Sample

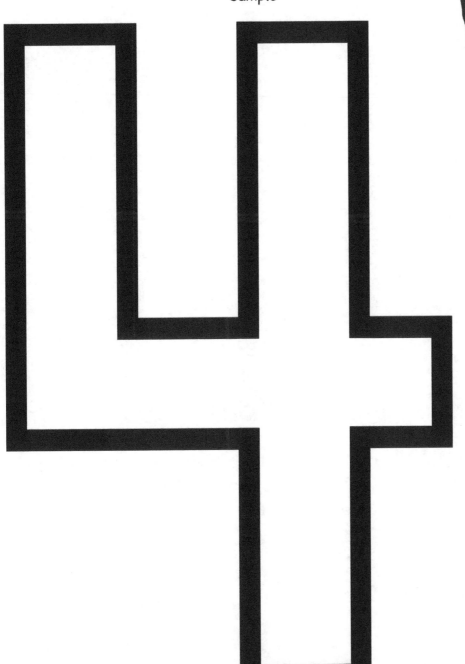

Trace the letters F and f with your finger. Can you see the letters Ff at the beginning of the words firefly, flowers, frog, fawn, and flamingo?

Firefly
firefly

Flowers
flowers

Frog
frog

Fawn
fawn

Flamingo
flamingo

Lesson 18 Math

Count each group. Draw lines to match the groups that are the same number.

Color the triangles brown and the circles yellow. The rest of the beach ball can be colored red, green, blue, black, or white.

Lesson 19 Bible

Draw a line from each animal to its shadow.

Circle the one that is different in each row.

Lesson 19 Phonics

Trace the letters F and f with your finger. Can you see the letters Ff at the beginning of the words fish, fox, frog, flying squirrel, and fly?

Aa Bb Cc Dd Ee Ff Gg Hh Ii Jj Kk Ll
Mm
Nn
Oo
Pp
Qq
Rr
Ss
Tt
Uu
Vv
Ww
Xx
Yy
Zz

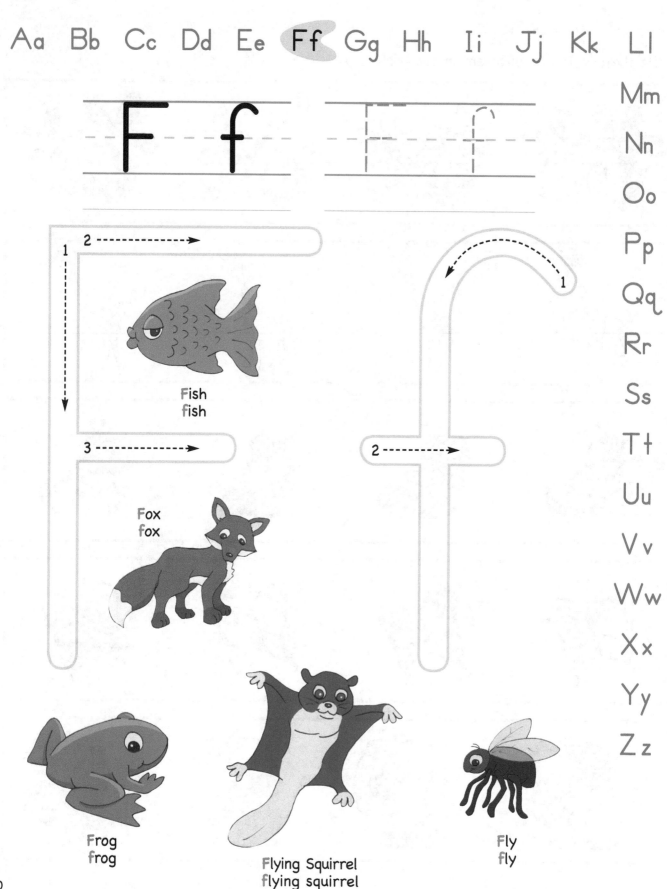

Fish
fish

Fox
fox

Frog
frog

Flying Squirrel
flying squirrel

Fly
fly

Use your finger to trace the large number 4. Count the animals and trace the number. Count the fish in each fishbowl and use a pencil to trace the number on the line next to the fishbowl.

1   2   3   4   5   6   7   8   9   10   11   12

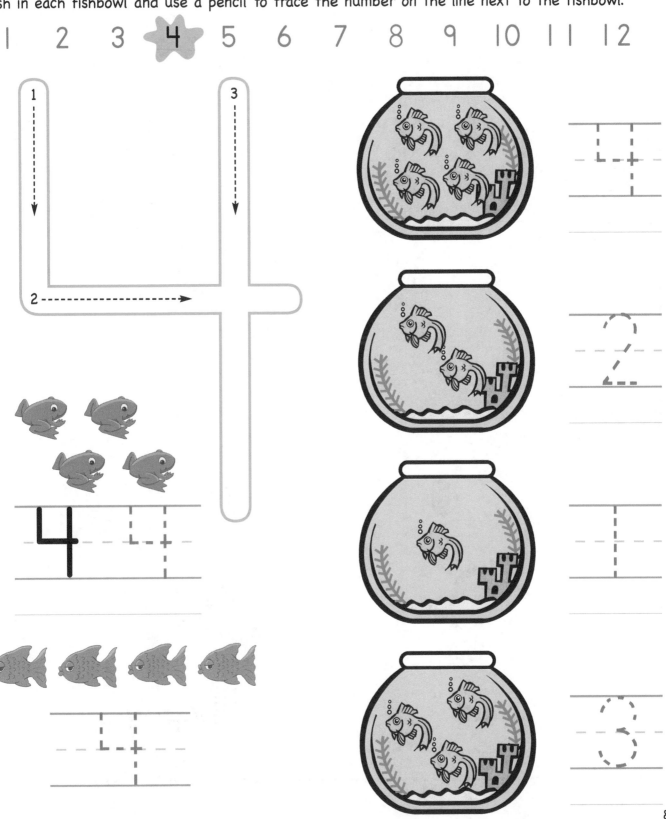

Lesson 19 Shapes

"The circle is one of my favorite shapes! Trace the circles, color the biggest circle yellow and color the smallest circle brown. Next, draw lines to complete the happy/mad faces."

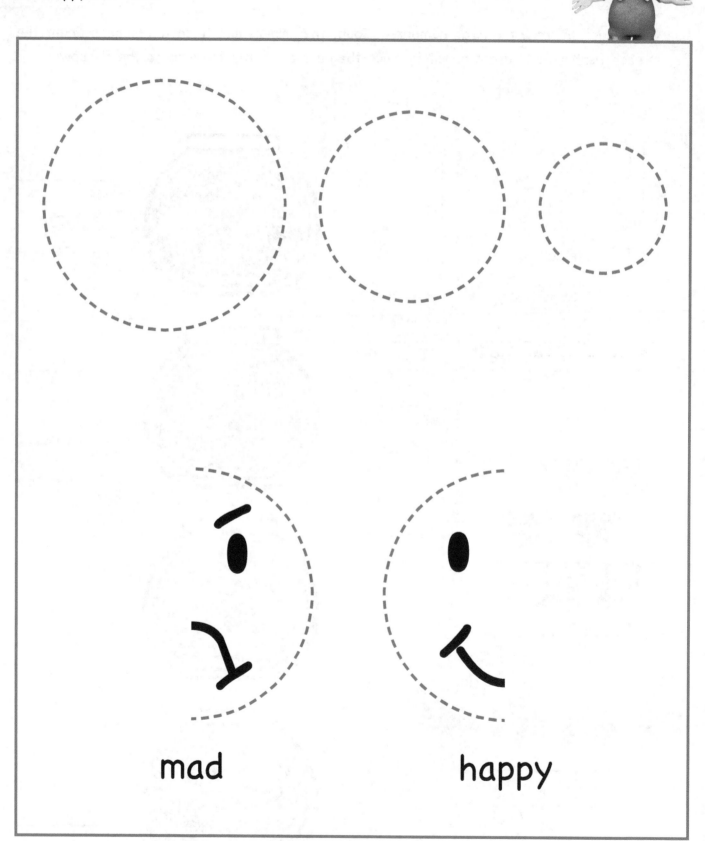

mad   happy

Students: Have a circle hunt at your house. Draw your favorite circle objects below.

Parents: Let the students find as many circles in their home as is possible. Then encourage them to draw their favorite objects in the space below. Return this homework page to school tomorrow.

Draw a black circle around Dd. Draw a yellow X on Ee. Draw a brown triangle around Ff.

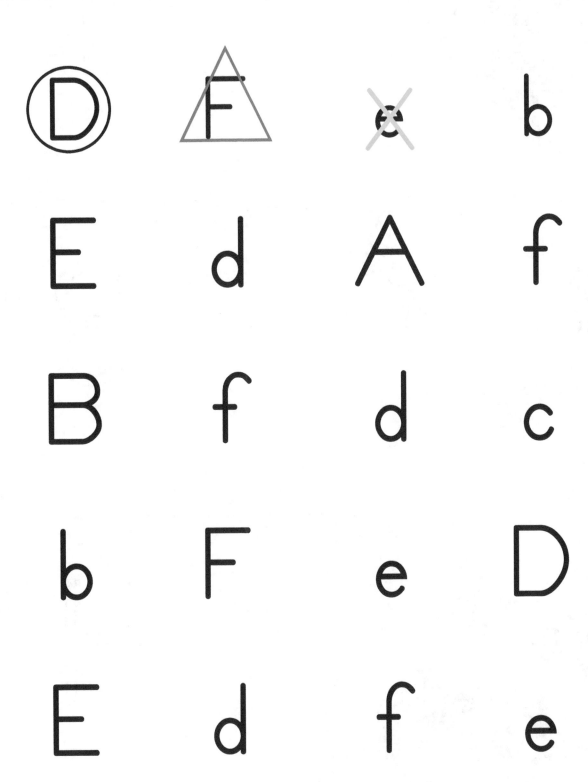

Lesson 20 Math

Count each group. Trace the numbers.

 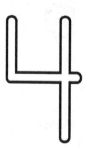

Color the large triangles green and the small triangles brown. Color the circles yellow and the rest of the picture any color you like.

87

Trace the letters G and g with your finger. Can you see the letters Gg at the beginning of the words gull, goldfish, grizzly, goat, and gopher?

Gull
gull

Goldfish
goldfish

Gopher
gopher

Grizzly
grizzly

Goat
goat

Use your finger to trace the large number **5**. Count the animals and use a pencil to trace the numbers on the lines.

1   2   3   4   **5**   6   7   8   9   10   11   12

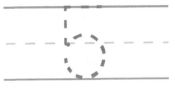

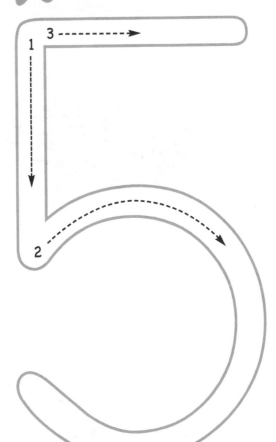

5

Read the number in each pom-pom. Put the correct number of dots on the clown hats. Color the hats.

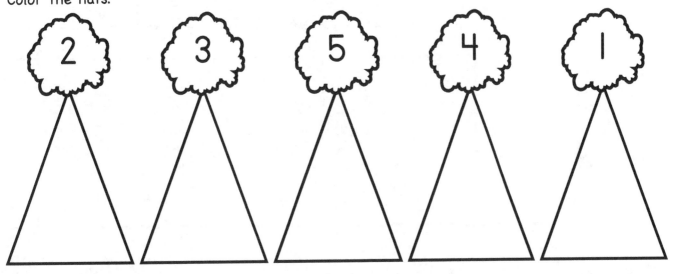

2   3   5   4   1

Count the items in each box. Draw a line to connect the number with the group that is the same.

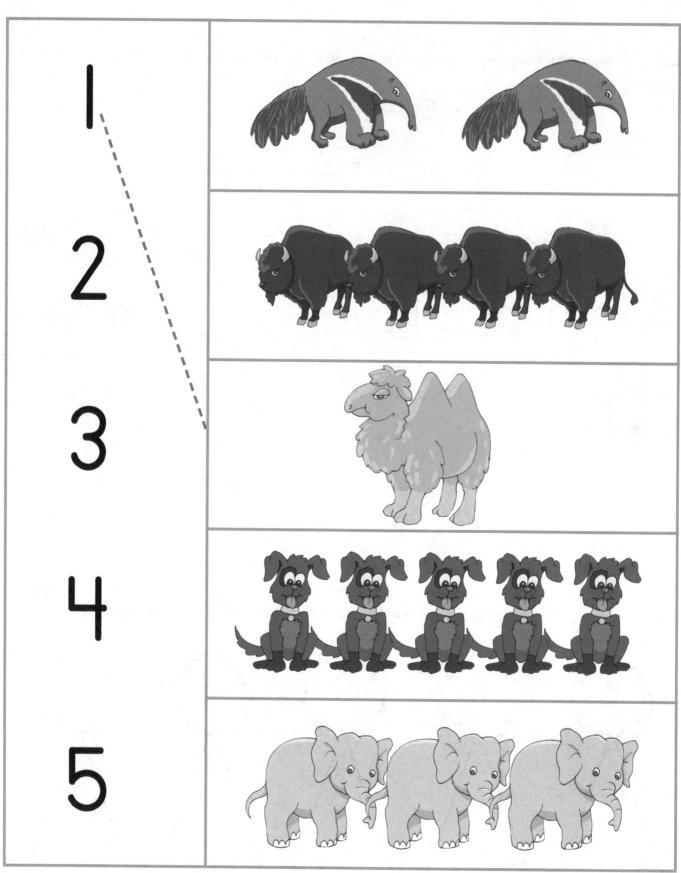

Color one turtle red. Color one turtle brown. Color one turtle your favorite color.

Color the butterfly wings on this page and the next. Cut them out and fold on the dotted line. Tape or glue the wings to a long balloon as illustrated by the sample.

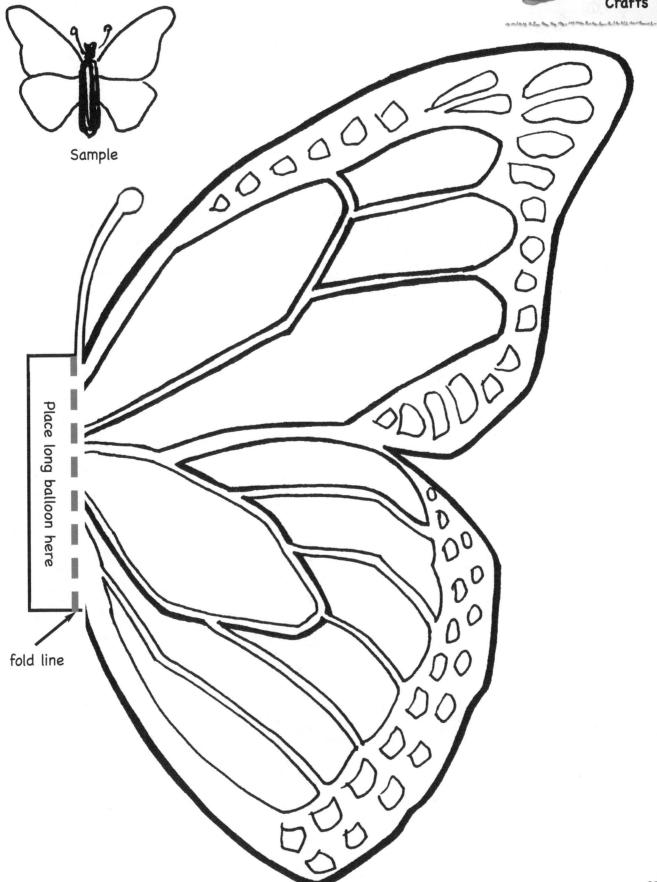

Sample

Place long balloon here

fold line

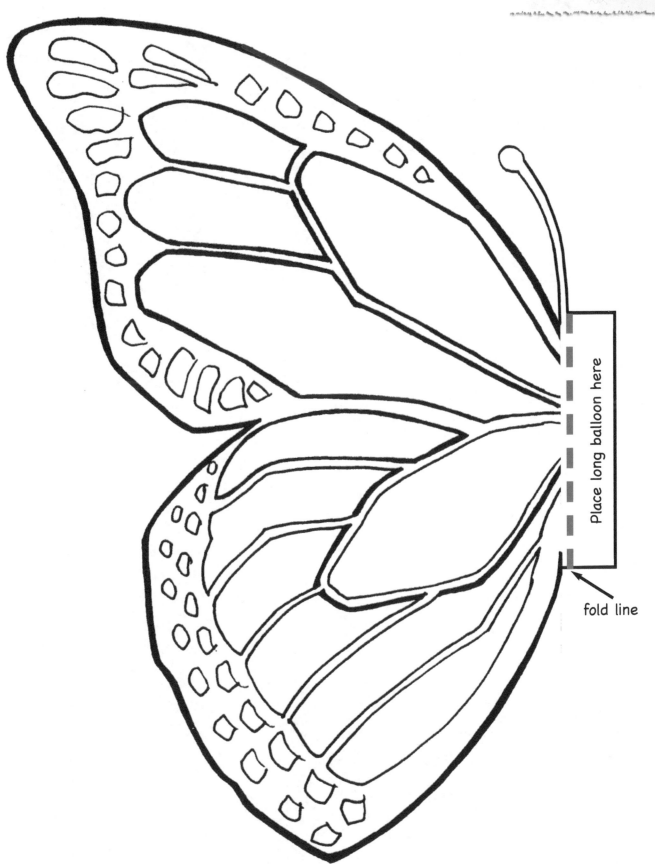

Place long balloon here

fold line

Cut out the items and glue them on a sheet of white construction paper as illustrated by the sample. Draw in the arms, legs, and face for the 5 David. Draw in the rest of the picture as illustrated by the sample.

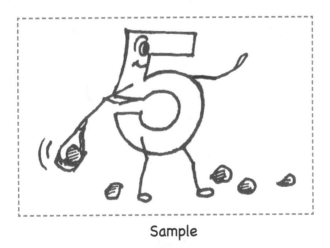

Sample

Count the items in each group. Draw a line to connect the number with the group that is the same.

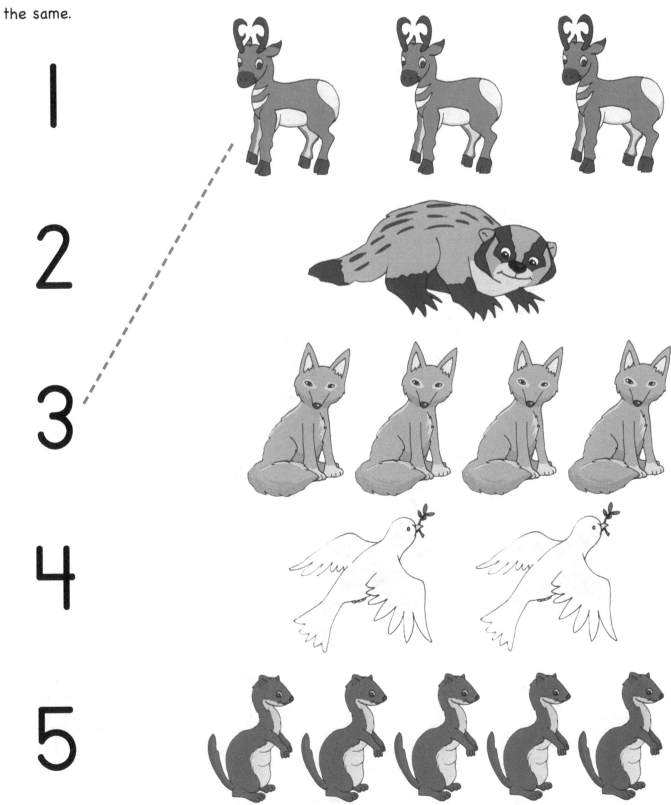

1

2

3

4

5

Lesson 23 Shapes

Name the shape of the balls. There are _____ circles.
Color the picture.

Trace the lines. Start at the top and trace to the bottom.

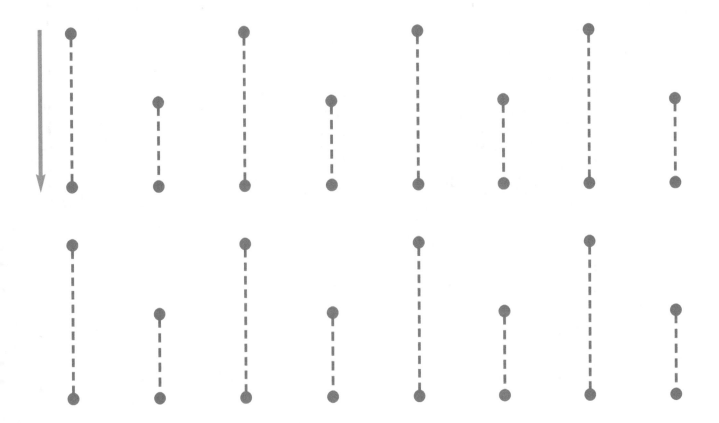

Start at the left and trace to the right.

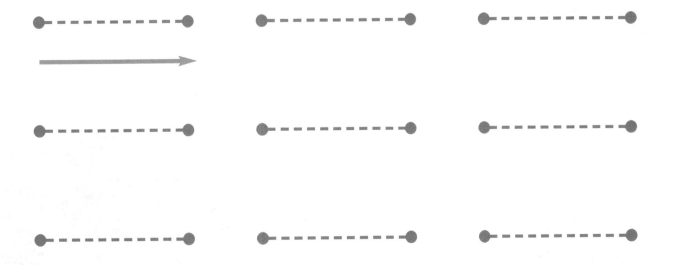

Lesson 24 Writing

Trace the straight lines to help Nancy find her way back to Agapeland.

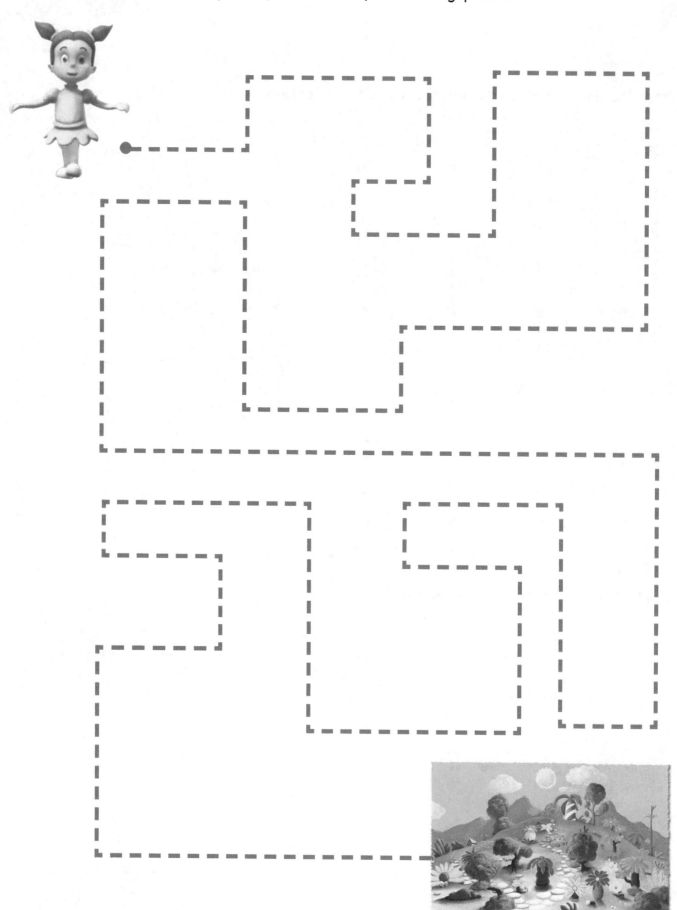

Trace the letters G and g with your finger. Can you see the letters Gg at the beginning of the words goat, gull, goose, gorilla, and grasshopper?

Aa Bb Cc Dd Ee Ff **Gg** Hh Ii Jj Kk Ll

G g

Mm

Nn

Oo

Pp

Qq

Rr

Ss

Tt

Uu

Vv

Ww

Xx

Yy

Zz

Goat
goat

Gull
gull

Goose
goose

Gorilla
gorilla

Grasshopper
grasshopper

103

Lesson 24 Math

Find the numbers 1, 2, 3, 4, and 5 on the drawing. Use a red crayon to connect the dots to make the picture. Color the picture.

Students: This experiment needs a magnifying glass. Go around your house and look at any place where dust gathers. Look at the dust with a magnifying glass. See if you can find anything interesting in the dust. Are there hairs? Pieces of lint? Bugs? Draw a picture of what you find. Bring to class tomorrow.

Parents: Every house has some corners where dust gathers. Your student is learning that the air around us carries dust and hair, lint, and cells. Let them do some exploring with your help.

Trace the letters H and h with your finger. Can you see the letters Hh at the beginning of the words hippo, hawk, heart, hedgehog, and hamster?

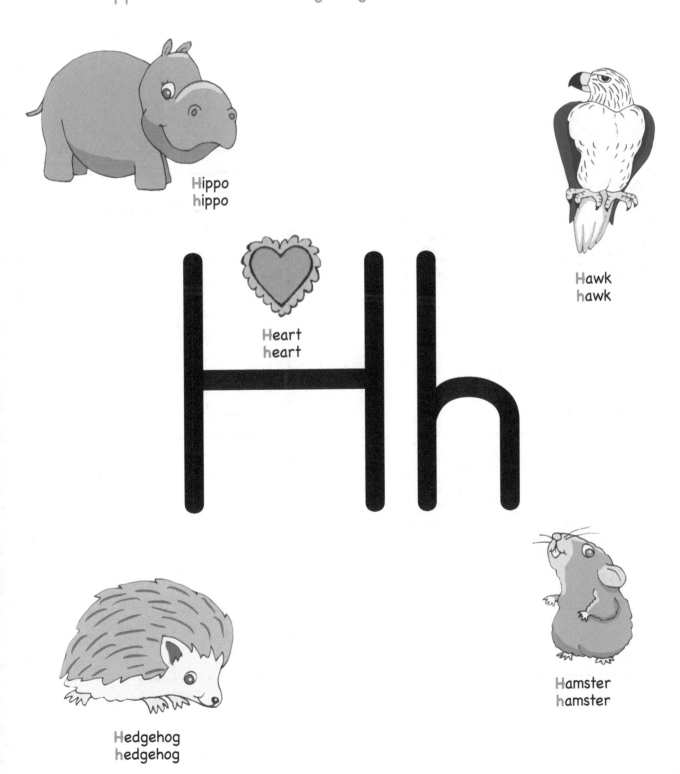

Hippo
hippo

Hawk
hawk

Heart
heart

Hamster
hamster

Hedgehog
hedgehog

Count the items in each box. Trace the numbers that count the items. Read and trace the numbers at the bottom of the page.

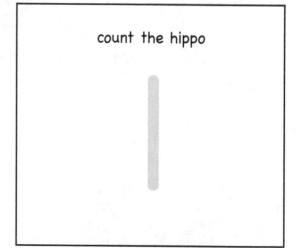

count the hippo

1

count the hens

3

count the hamsters

5

1 2 3 4 5

What shape is the earth? Point out the areas that are water and those that are land.
Color the land areas brown and the water areas blue.

Lesson 26 Math

Count the items in each group. Trace the lines to connect groups with the same number of items.

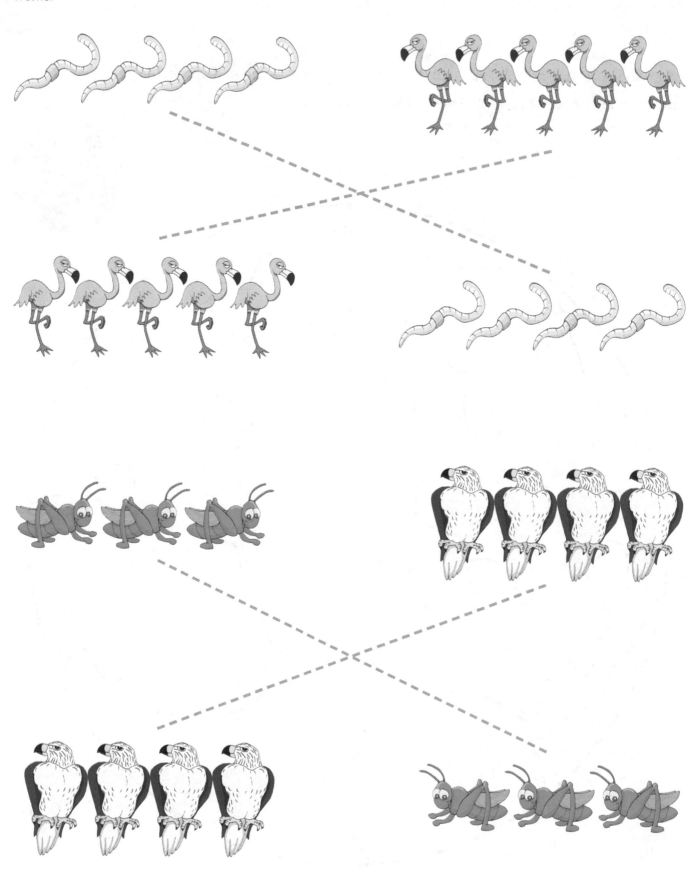

Trace the letters H and h with your finger. Can you see the letters H h at the beginning of the words humpback whale, hummingbird, hyena, hedgehog, and hen?

Aa Bb Cc Dd Ee Ff Gg **Hh** Ii Jj Kk Ll

Mm

Nn

Oo

Pp

Qq

Rr

Ss

Tt

Uu

Vv

Ww

Xx

Yy

Zz

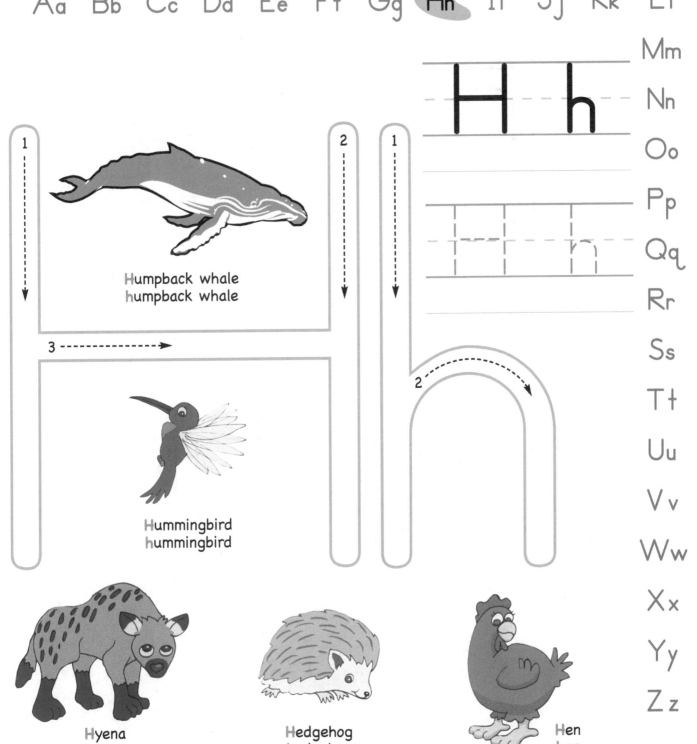

Humpback whale
humpback whale

Hummingbird
hummingbird

Hyena
hyena

Hedgehog
hedgehog

Hen
hen

111

Make a cross by drawing between the lines. Trace the spiral by starting in the center and following the dotted lines. Trace the straight lines on the bottom of the page.

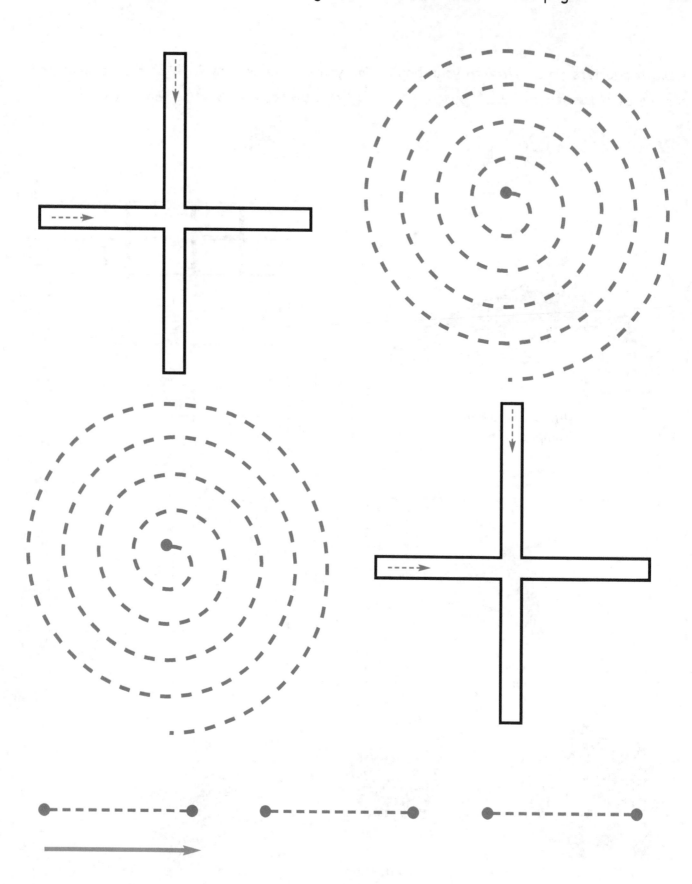

Cut out the number strip at the bottom of the page. Count the items in each group.
Paste the correct number in each box.

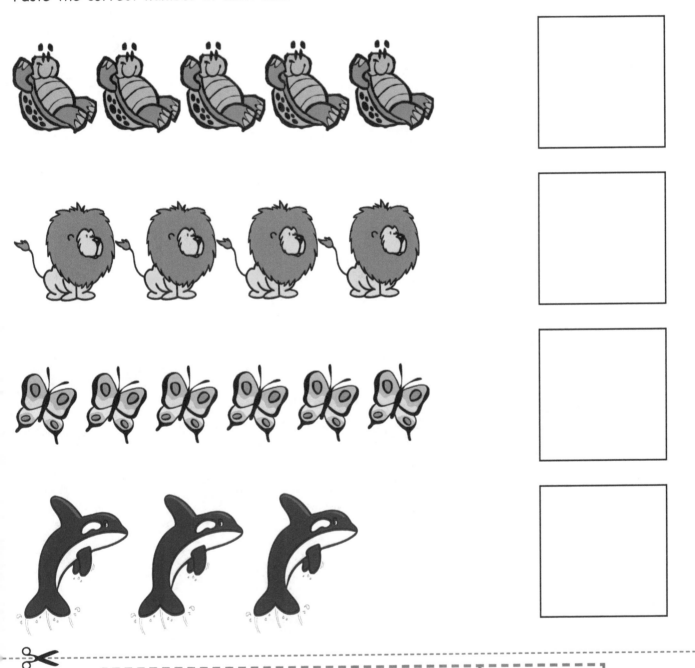

$$3 \quad 4 \quad 5 \quad 6$$

Color and cut out the pictures below. Paste the circles ABOVE the line.
Paste the triangles UNDER the line.

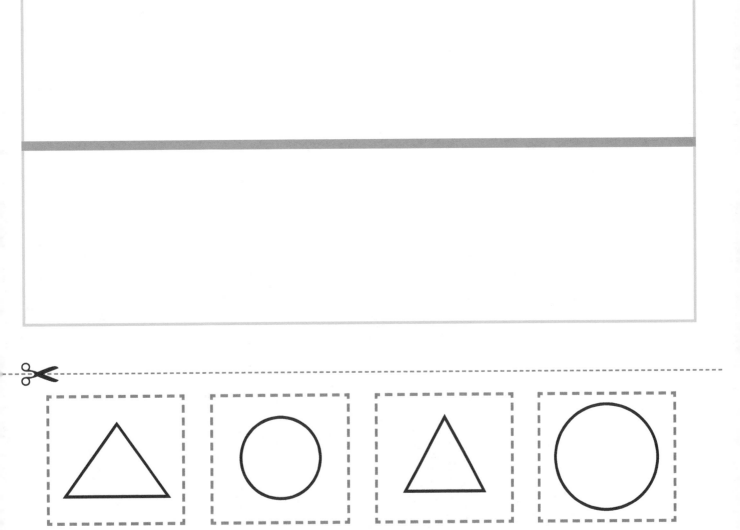

✂ -

Cut out the items and glue them on a sheet of white construction paper as illustrated by the sample. Draw in the arms, legs, and face for the **6** creation man. Draw in the rest of the picture as illustrated in the sample.

Sample

Trace the letters I and i with your finger. Can you see the letters Ii at the beginning of the words iguana, insects, ibex, ibis, and impala?

Iguana
iguana

Insects
insects

Ibex
ibex

Ibis
ibis

Impala
impala

Trace the square. You may color the square.

square

Use your finger to trace the large number 6. Count the animals and use a pencil to trace the numbers on the lines.

1   2   3   4   5   6   7   8   9   10   11   12

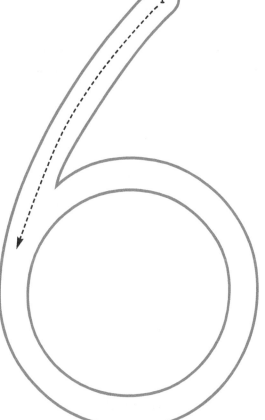

6

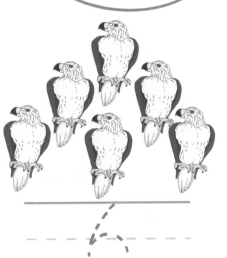

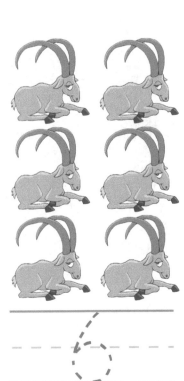

Lesson 28 Writing

Make a cross by drawing between lines. Trace the spiral by starting in the center and following the dotted lines. Trace the circle and the square.

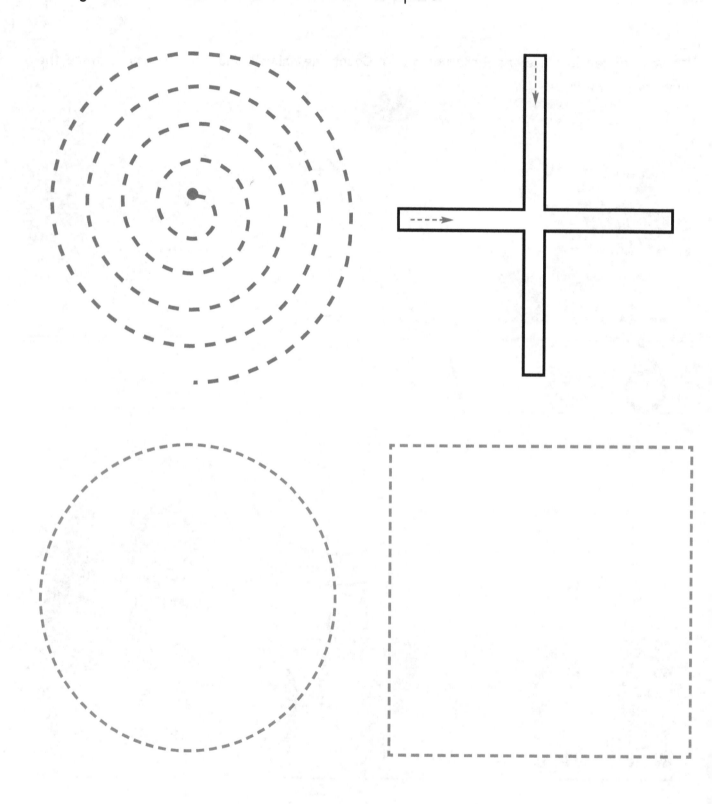

Color the squares, cut them out, and paste them on the train.

✂ -

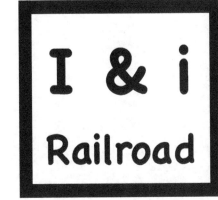

I & i
Railroad

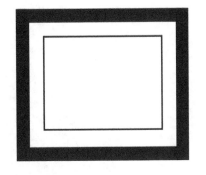

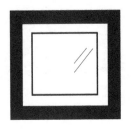

123

Trace the letters I and i with your finger. Can you see the letters Ii at the beginning of the words ibex, impala, ice cream, iguana, insects, and ibis?

Aa Bb Cc Dd Ee Ff Gg Hh **Ii** Jj Kk Ll
Mm
Nn
Oo
Pp
Qq
Rr
Ss
Tt
Uu
Vv
Ww
Xx
Yy
Zz

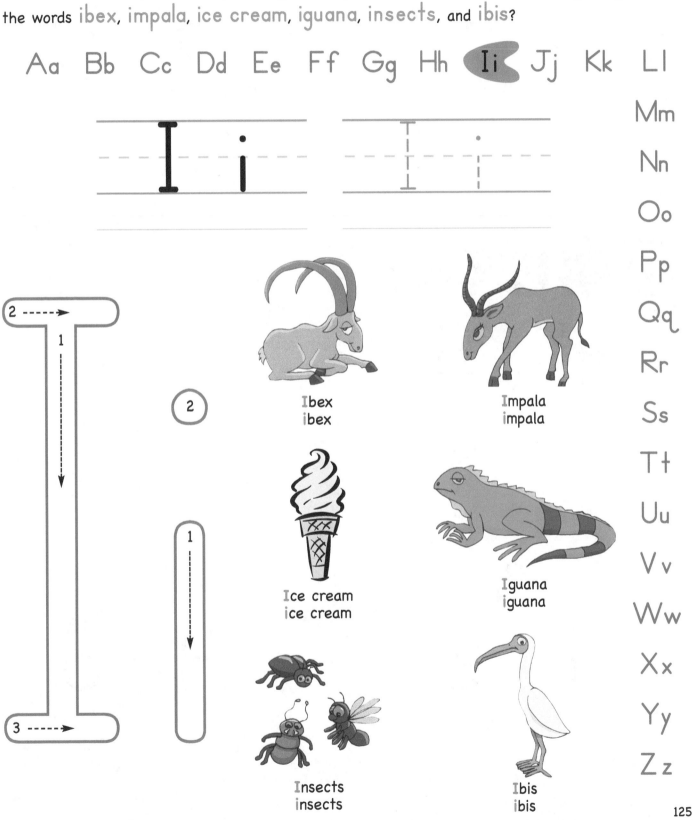

Ibex
ibex

Impala
impala

Ice cream
ice cream

Iguana
iguana

Insects
insects

Ibis
ibis

Count each group and circle the correct number.

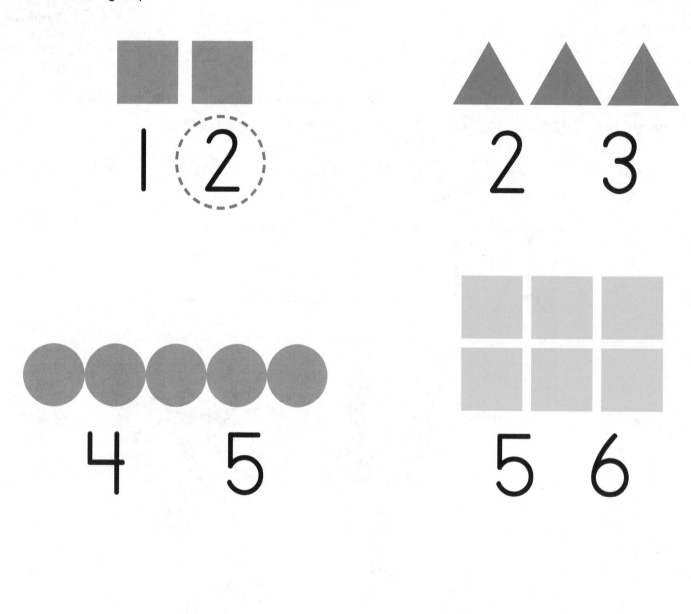

Cut out the parts of the animals. Glue them on another piece of paper.
What animals did you find? Color the animals.

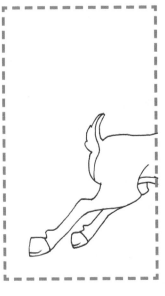

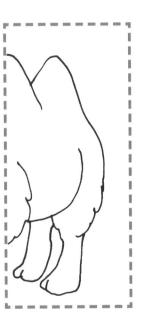

Students: Look around your home. Find three things that are squares. Draw them on this sheet and return to class tomorrow.

Parents: Help the students with the instructions.

Color the crown. Glue gems on the crown. Cut out the crown. Glue, tape, or staple the strips together.

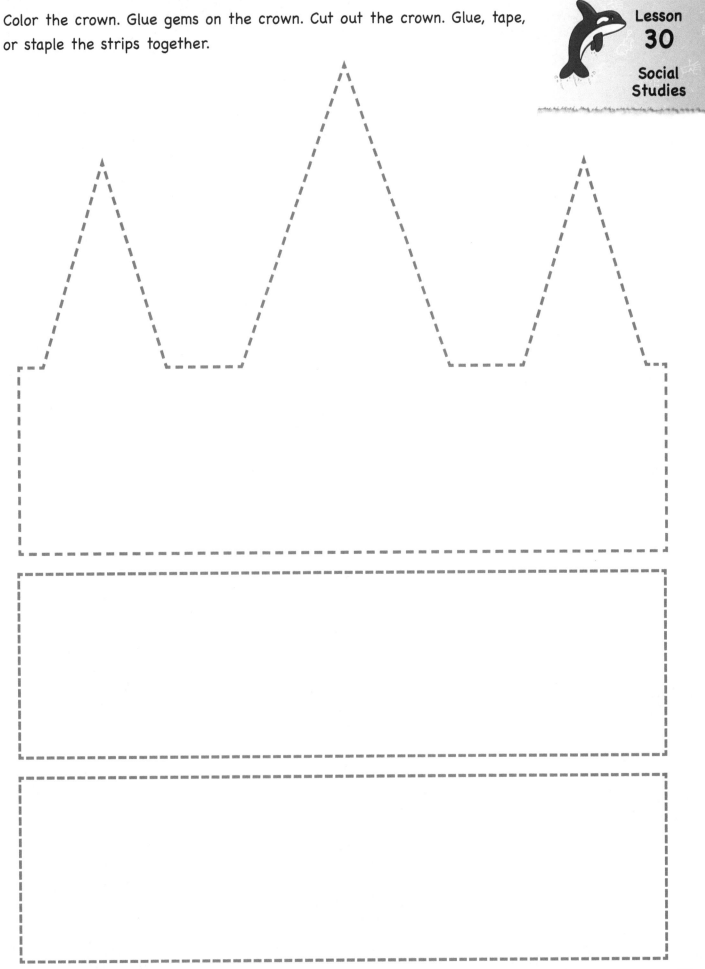

Draw a pink triangle around G g. Draw a blue circle around H h. Make a white X on I i.

   f

h   g   F   H

i   A   I   G

G   i   H   d

Lesson 30 Math

Trace the numbers. Count the items in each box. Draw a line between the picture and the number that matches.

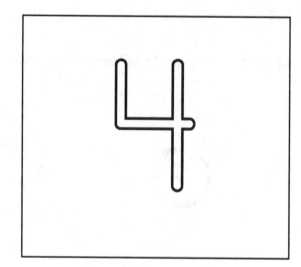

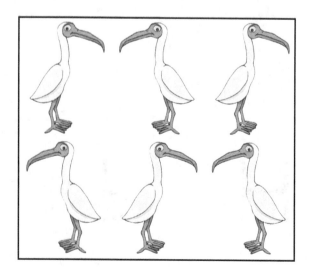

Count the squares in the picture. There are _____ squares. Color the picture.
Color at least one square purple.

Trace the letters J and j with your finger. Can you see the letters Jj at the beginning of the words jerboa, jackrabbit, jaguar, and jackal?

Jerboa
jerboa

Jackrabbit
jackrabbit

Jaguar
jaguar

Jackal
jackal

137

Lesson 31 Math

Use your finger to trace the large number 7. Count the animals and use a pencil to trace the numbers on the lines.

1   2   3   4   5   6   **7**   8   9   10   11   12

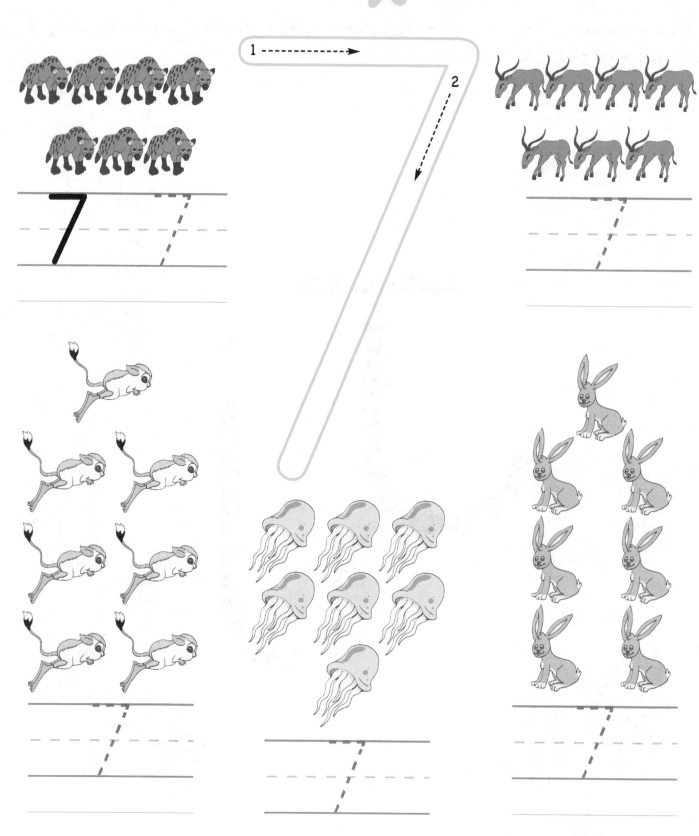

Cut out the number strip. Count each group and paste the correct number in each box.

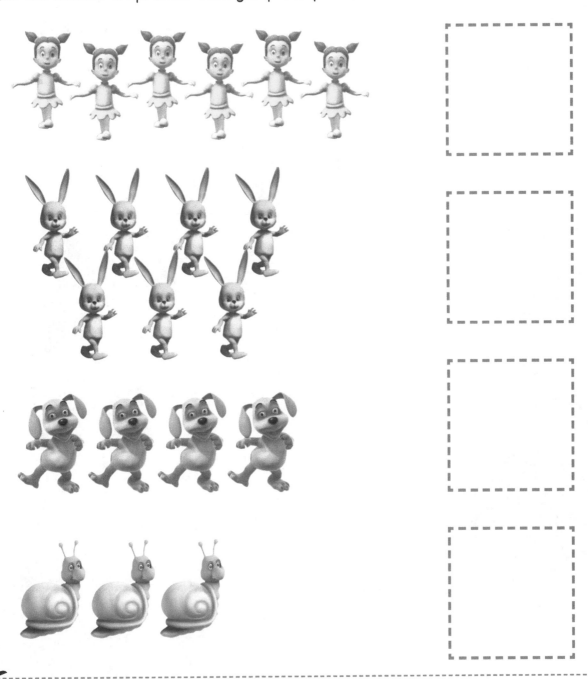

Lesson 32 Shapes

Trace the squares, color the large square purple and color the small square pink. Complete the square on the bottom of the page and decorate it to make it look like a birthday present.

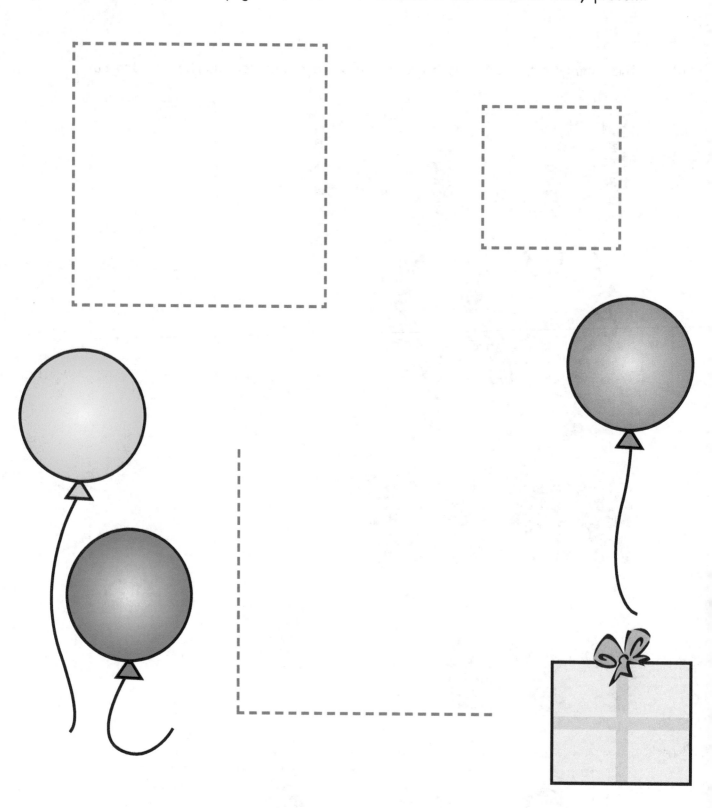

Cut out the items on the worksheet and glue them to construction paper as illustrated by the sample. Draw in the arms and face for the 7 dipping man. Draw in the rest of the picture.

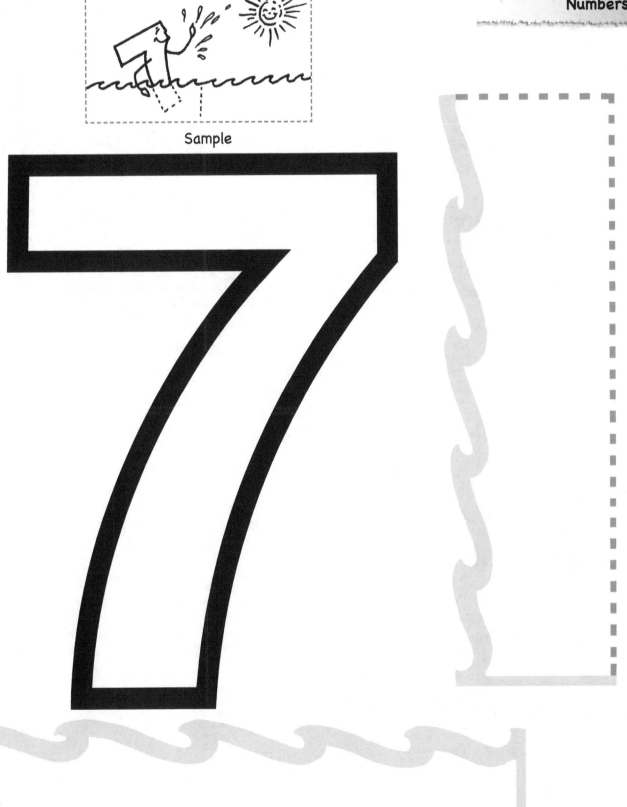

Sample

Count each group of items and circle the correct number under the items.

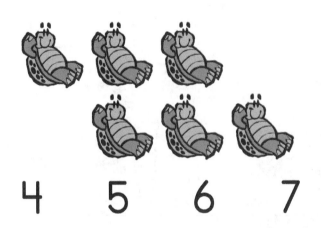

4   5   6   7

4   5   6   7

4   5   6   7

4   5   6   7

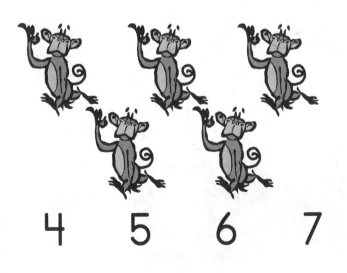

4   5   6   7

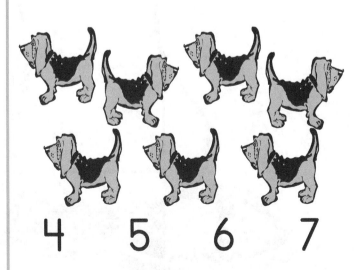

4   5   6   7

Lesson 33 Shapes

Color the large squares yellow, the small squares green, and the rest of the picture any other colors.

Trace the letters J and j with your finger. Can you see the letters Jj at the beginning of the words jellyfish, jay, jackal, and jet?

Aa Bb Cc Dd Ee Ff Gg Hh Ii **Jj** Kk Ll
Mm
Nn
Oo
Pp
Qq
Rr
Ss
Tt
Uu
Vv
Ww
Xx
Yy
Zz

J j

2 →
1
2

1

Jellyfish
jellyfish

Jay
jay

Jackal
jackal

Jet
jet

145

Count each group of items and draw a line to the correct number.

3

6

5

7

Cut out the parts of the animal. Put the pieces together.
What animal did you find?

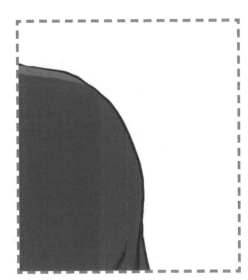

Trace the letters K and k with your finger. Can you see the letters Kk at the beginning of the words killdeer, kingfisher, kangaroo, kinkajou, and kitten?

Killdeer
killdeer

Kingfisher
kingfisher

Kangaroo
kangaroo

Kinkajou
kinkajou

Kitten
kitten

Lesson 35 Math

Trace the numbers. Count each group of items and draw a line to the correct number.

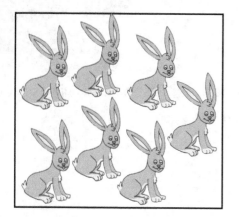

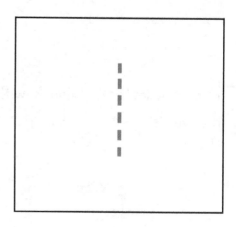

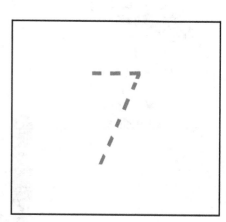

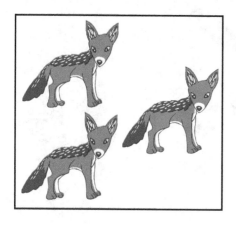

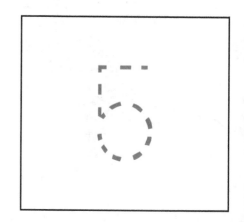

Count the squares. Count the circles. Count both squares and circles. How many squares and circles are there altogether? Color the squares green, color the circles red, and then color the party hat black.

Lesson 36a Math

Use your finger to trace the large number 8. Count the animals and use a pencil to trace the numbers on the lines.

1   2   3   4   5   6   7   8   9   10   11   12

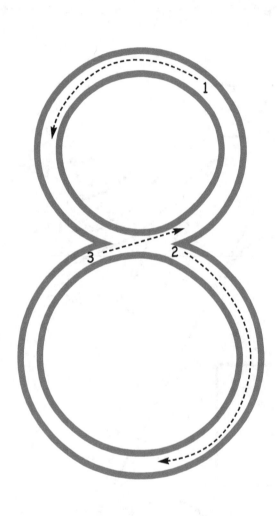

8

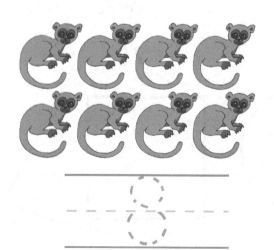

Name

Count each group. Draw a line to the group that matches.

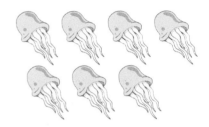

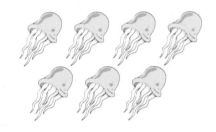

Lesson 36 Shapes

Count the squares, count the circles, and then count how many squares and circles there are altogether. Color the squares purple, the circles green, and the teapot yellow.

Trace the letters K and k with your finger. Can you see the letters Kk at the beginning of the words kudu, killer whale, and koala?

Aa Bb Cc Dd Ee Ff Gg Hh Ii Jj **Kk** Ll
Mm
Nn
Oo
Pp
Qq
Rr
Ss
Tt
Uu
Vv
Ww
Xx
Yy
Zz

Kudu
kudu

Killer Whale
killer whale

Koala
koala

155

Count the objects in each group. Draw a line to the correct number.

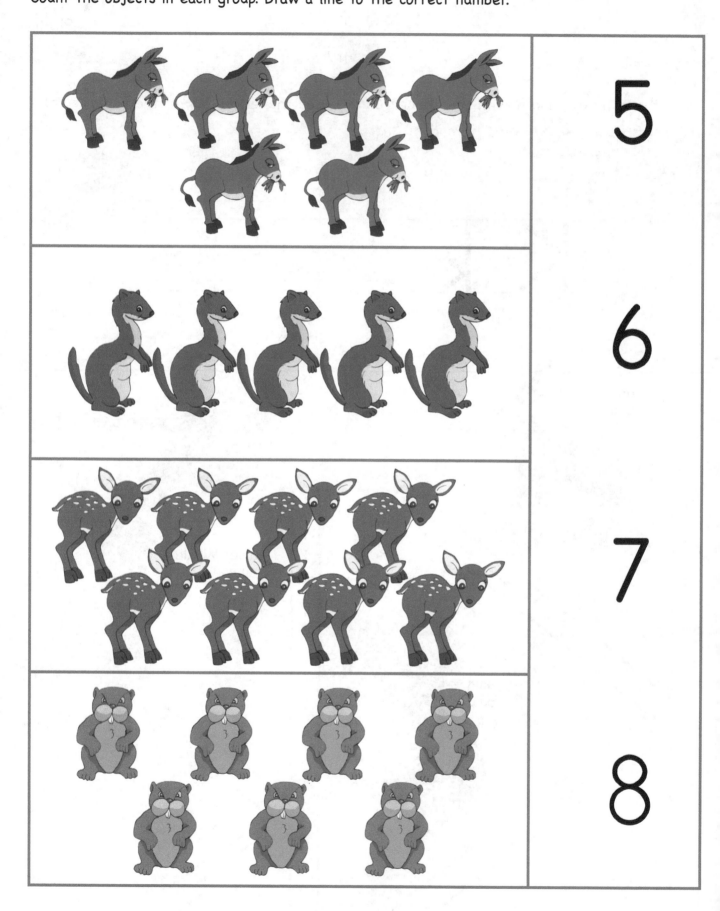

Cut out the items on the worksheet and glue them to construction paper as illustrated by the sample. Draw in the arms, legs, and face for the 8 king. Draw in the rest of the picture.

Sample

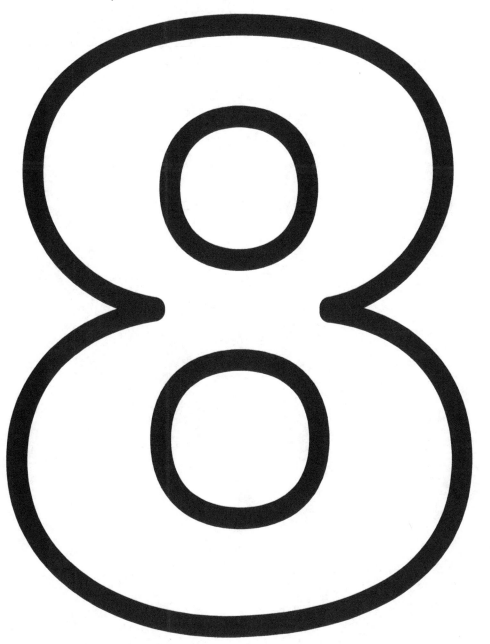

Trace the letters ⌴ and ⎮ with your finger. Can you see the letters ⌴⎮ at the beginning of the words ladybug, lizard, lamb, and lobster?

Ladybug
ladybug

Lizard
lizard

Lamb
lamb

Lobster
lobster

Count each group of items and circle the correct number under the items.

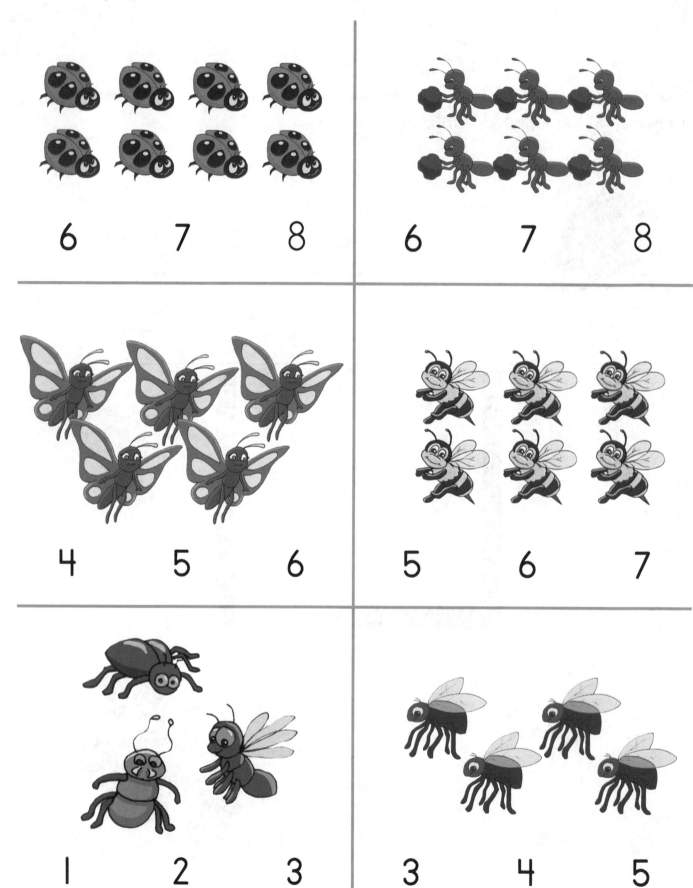

6 7 8

6 7 8

4 5 6

5 6 7

1 2 3

3 4 5

Name

Draw lines to connect pictures that look the same. You may color the pictures as you like.

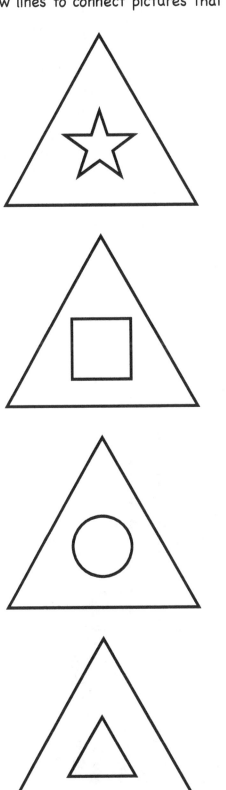

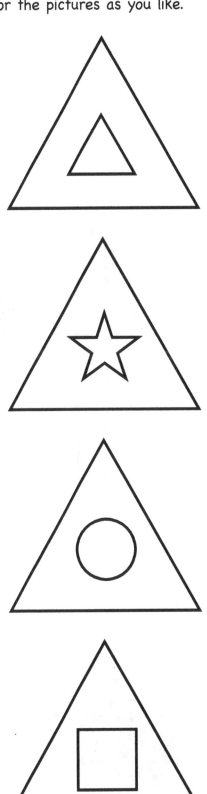

Lesson 39 Phonics

Trace the letters L and l with your finger. Can you see the letters Ll at the beginning of the words lion, leopard, lynx, and llama?

Aa Bb Cc Dd Ee Ff Gg Hh Ii Jj Kk **Ll**

Mm
Nn
Oo
Pp
Qq
Rr
Ss
Tt
Uu
Vv
Ww
Xx
Yy
Zz

Lion
lion

Leopard
leopard

Lynx
lynx

Llama
llama

Students: Gather your family and sing "America the Beautiful" together. Explain to your family what you learned about the WAVES OF GRAIN.

Parents: Encourage your student to memorize "America the Beautiful." The students have been learning about grasses and types of grain.

America the Beautiful

Oh, Beautiful for spacious skies
For amber WAVES OF GRAIN
For purple mountains majesties
Above the fruited plain

America, America
God shed His grace on thee
And crown thy good with brotherhood
From sea to shining sea.

Lesson 39 Math

Trace the numbers. Count each group of items and draw a line to the correct number.

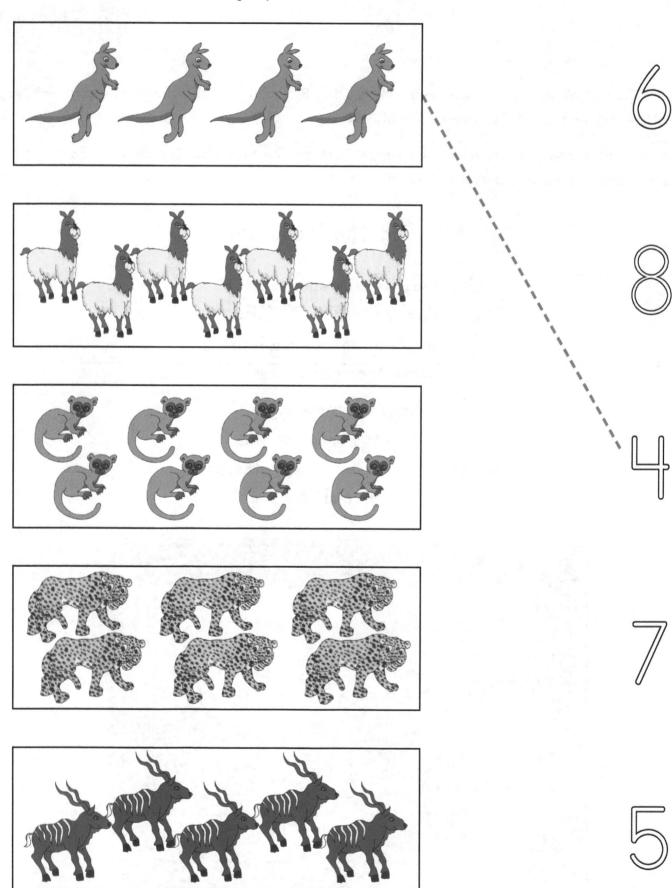

Cut out the parts of the animal. Put the pieces together.
What animal did you find?

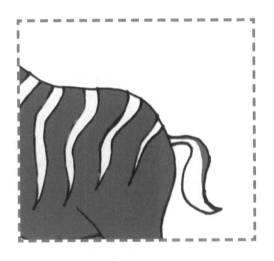

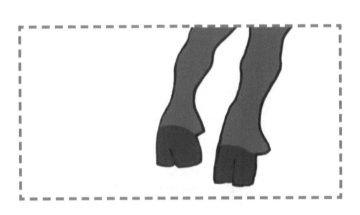

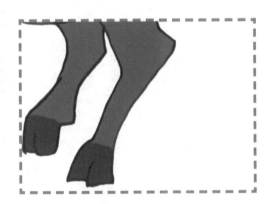

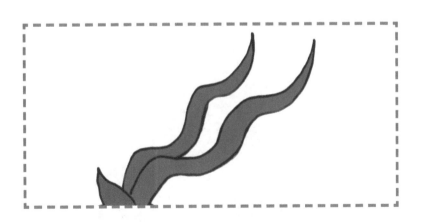

Draw an orange square around the J j letters, a purple circle around the K k letters, and a yellow triangle around the L l letters.

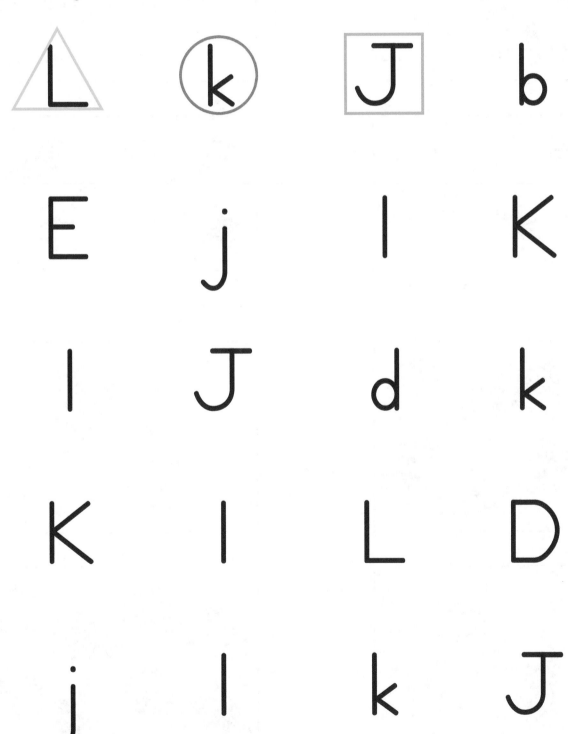

Lesson 40 Math

Count each group and then draw a line to match groups with the same number.

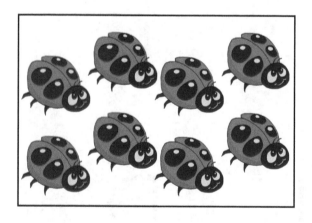

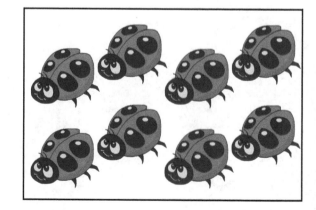

Look for the circle, the square, and the dotted lines on the worksheet. Cut from the circle to the square, following the dotted lines as closely as you can.

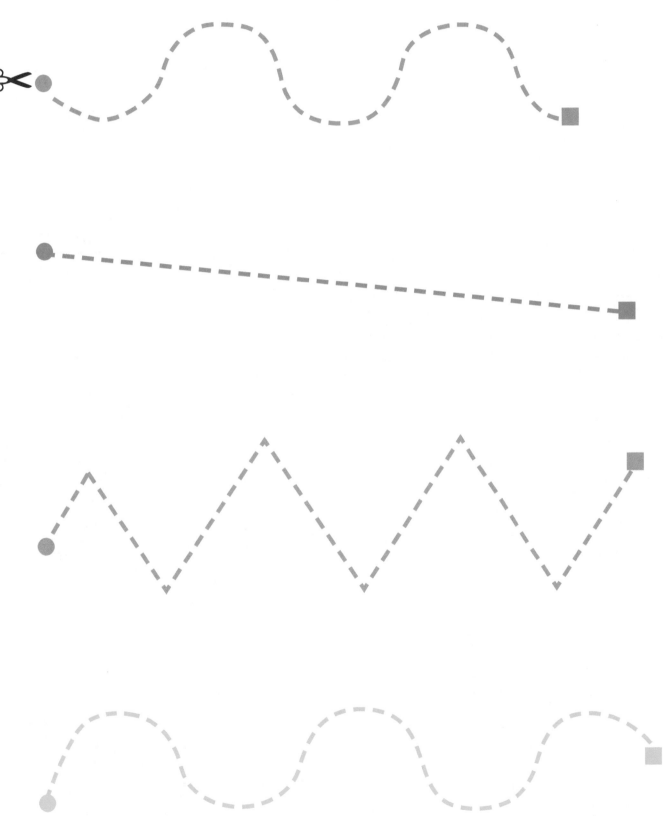

Trace the letters M and m with your finger. Can you see the letters Mm at the beginning of the words mosquito, moth, mink, monkey, and moose?

Mosquito
mosquito

Moth
moth

Mink
mink

Monkey
monkey

Moose
moose

Use your finger to trace the large number 9. Count the insects and use a pencil to trace the numbers on the lines.

1 2 3 4 5 6 7 8 9 10 11 12

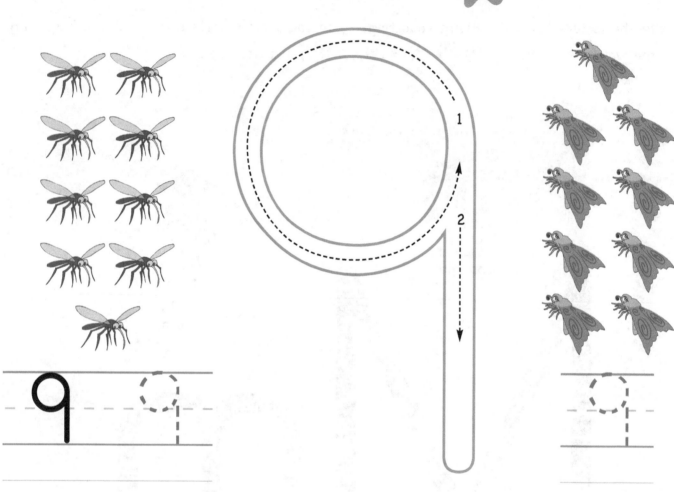

Count each group. Draw a line to the group that matches.

Name

Color the shapes at the bottom of the sheet, cut them out, and paste them under the correct group.

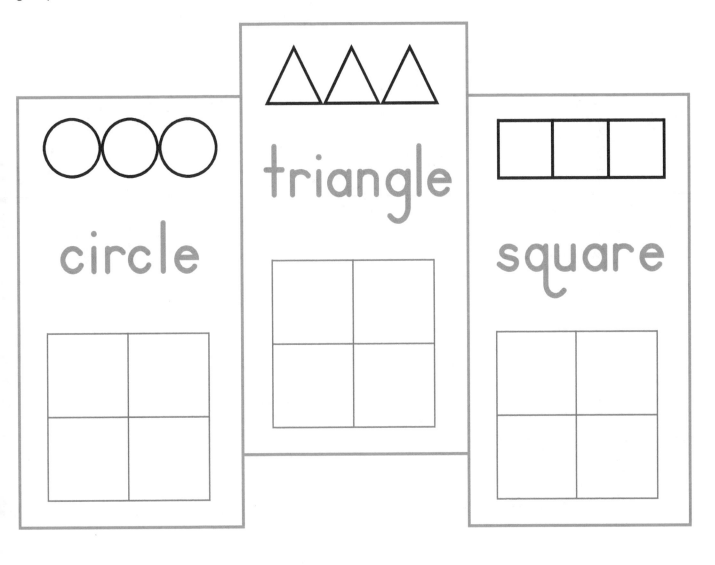

circle

triangle

square

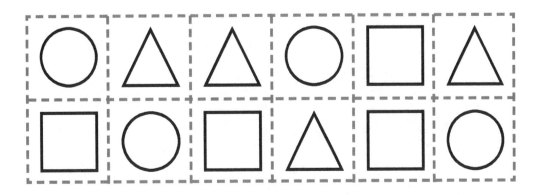

Trace the letters M and m with your finger. Can you see the letters Mm at the beginning of the words muskrat, mink, moose, mouse, and muskox?

Aa Bb Cc Dd Ee Ff Gg Hh Ii Jj Kk Ll

M m   M m

Mm

Nn

Oo

Pp

Qq

Rr

Ss

Tt

Uu

Vv

Ww

Xx

Yy

Zz

Muskrat
muskrat

Mink
mink

Moose
moose

Mouse
mouse

Muskox
muskox

Lesson 42 Math

Find the numbers 1 to 9. Connect the dots to complete the drawing. Color the drawing.

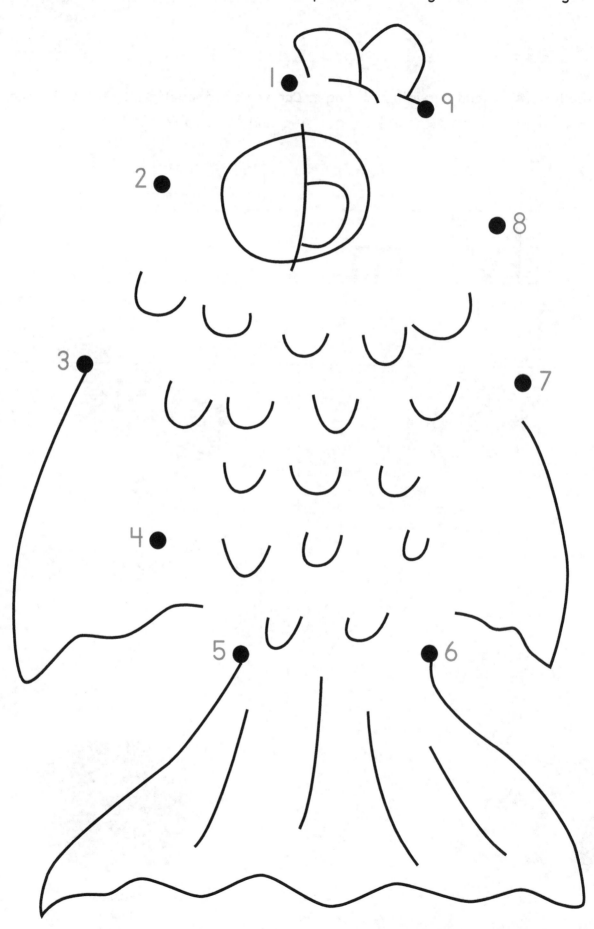

Cut out the items on the worksheet and glue them to construction paper as illustrated by the sample. Draw in the arms, legs, and face for the 9 happy man. Draw in the rest of the picture.

Sample

Trace the letters N and n with your finger. Can you see the letters Nn at the beginning of the words nutria, nyala, newt, and narwhal?

Nutria
nutria

Nyala
nyala

Newt
newt

Narwhal
narwhal

179

Draw candles on the cupcakes to match the number. Color the cupcakes.

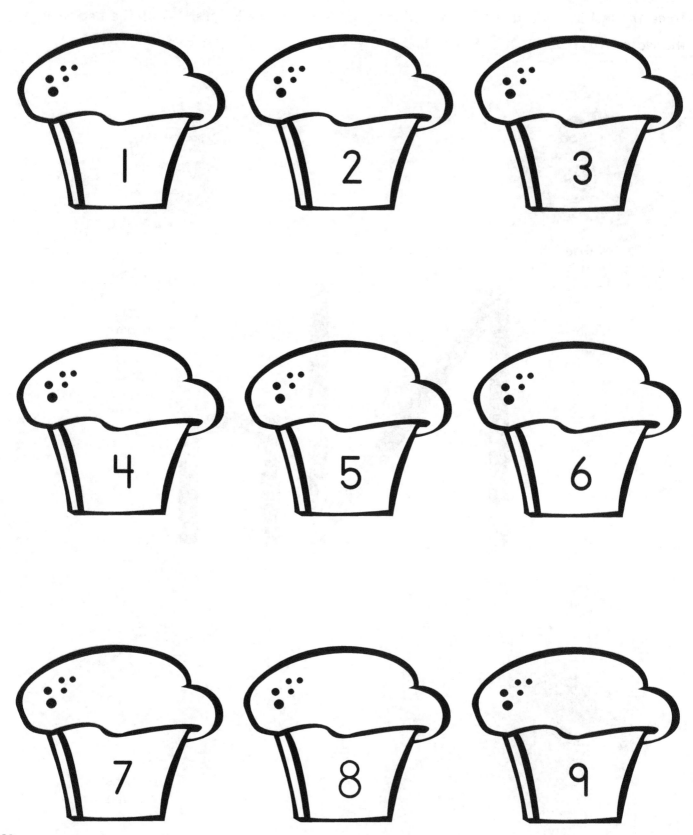

Trace the rectangle. You may color the rectangle.

rectangle

Lesson 43b Shapes

Count the rectangles. There are _____ rectangles.
Color the picture. Make some of the rectangles gray.

Trace the letters N and n with your finger. Can you see the letters Nn at the beginning of the words nilgai, nuthatch, numbat, and newt?

Aa Bb Cc Dd Ee Ff Gg Hh Ii Jj Kk Ll

Mm

Nn

Oo

Pp

Qq

Rr

Ss

Tt

Uu

Vv

Ww

Xx

Yy

Zz

N n   N n

Nilgai
nilgai

Nuthatch
nuthatch

Numbat
numbat

Newt
newt

183

Lesson 44 Math

Connect the dots to complete the drawing so that Nancy can go **up** the steps.

What shapes are under the steps? What is the opposite of up?

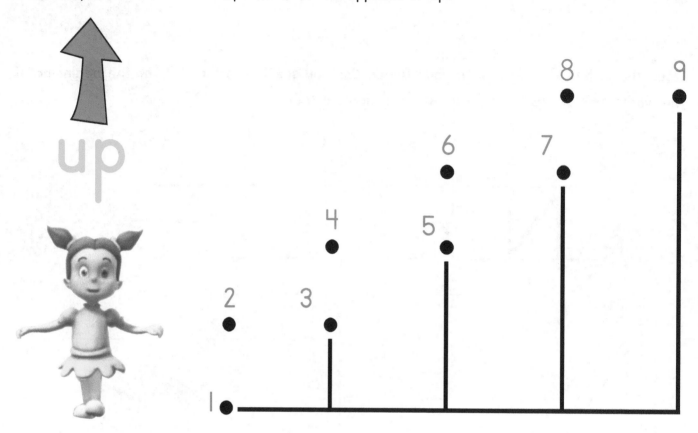

Connect the dots to complete the drawing so that Smuggles can go **down** the steps.

What is the opposite of down?

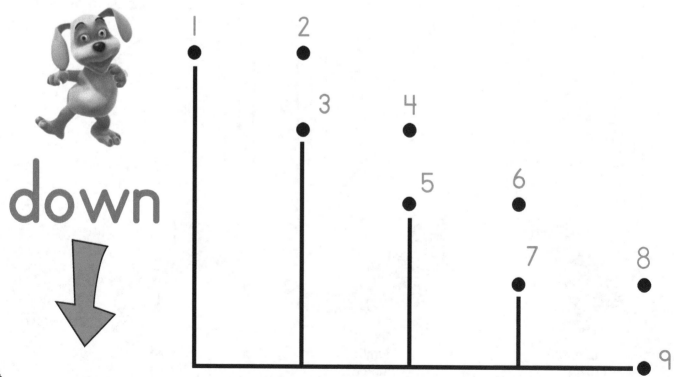

184

Cut out the parts of the animal. Put the pieces together.
What animal did you find?

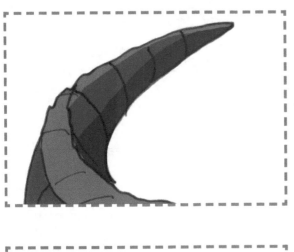

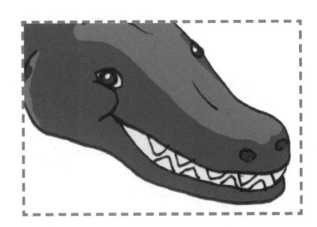

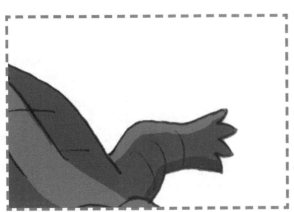

Trace the numbers. Count each group of items and draw a line to the correct number.

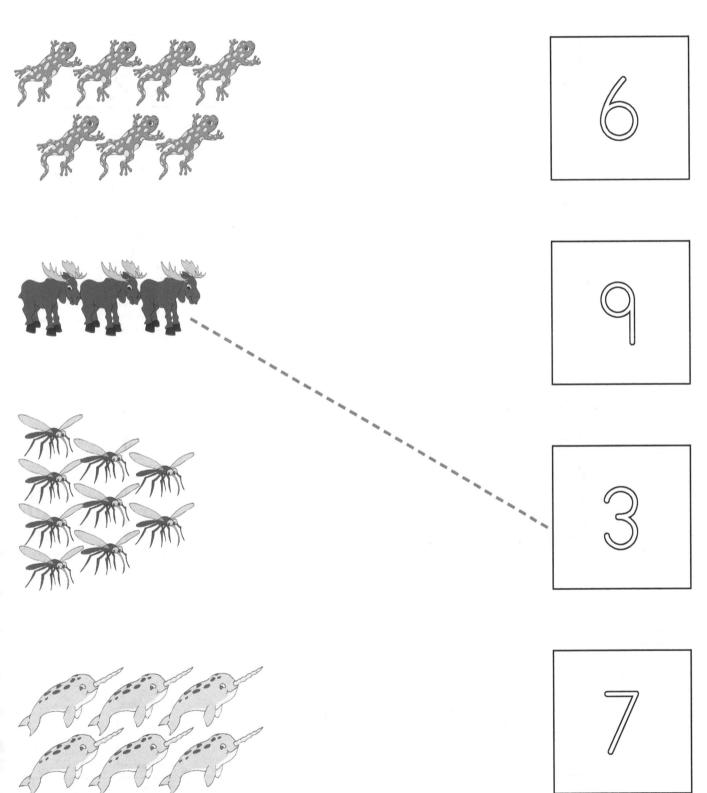

Lesson 45 Shapes

Count the shapes on the sheet that are the same. Draw lines to connect the rectangles that are the same inside. You may color the pictures as you like.

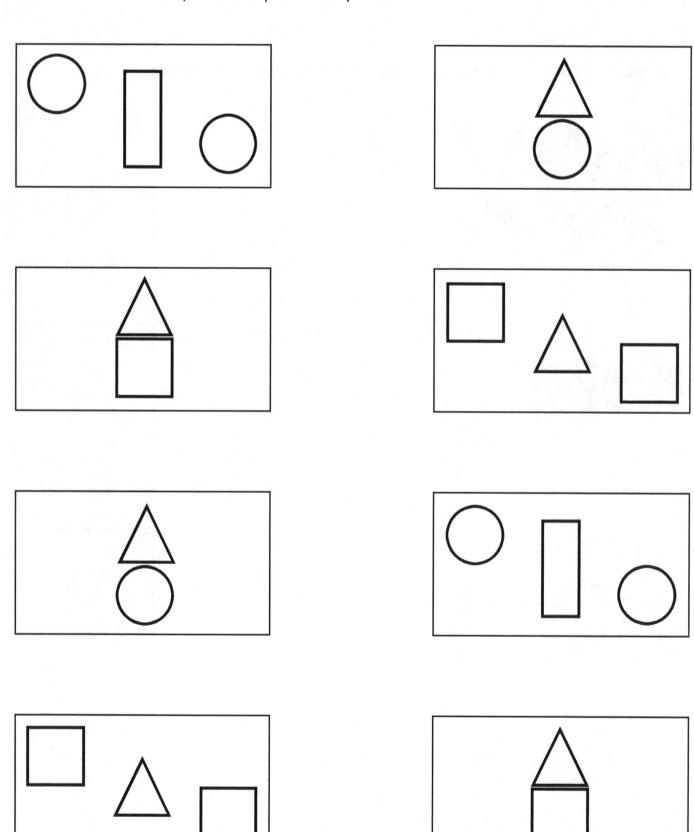

Trace the letters ◯ and o with your finger. Can you see the letters ◯o at the beginning of the words opossum, ostrich, owl, osprey, and oyster?

Opossum
opossum

Ostrich
ostrich

Owl
owl

Osprey
osprey

Oyster
oyster

189

Lesson 46 Math

Count each group. Draw a line to the group that matches.

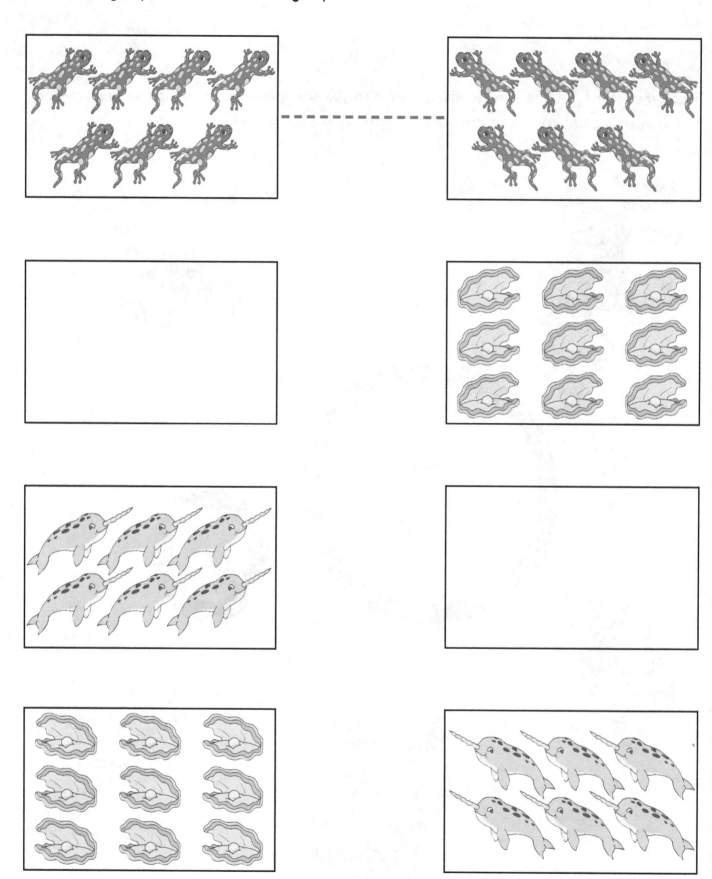

Connect the dots from 0 to 9 to form the tree trunk. Color the picture.

Use your finger to trace the large number 0. Count the items in each box and use a pencil to trace the numbers on the lines.

0 1 2 3 4 5 6 7 8 9 10 11 12

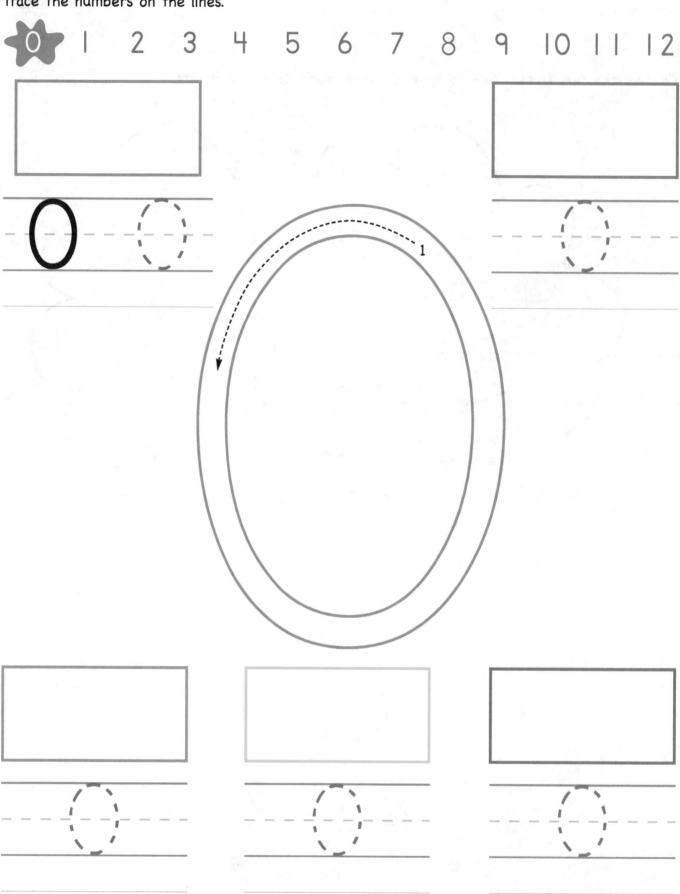

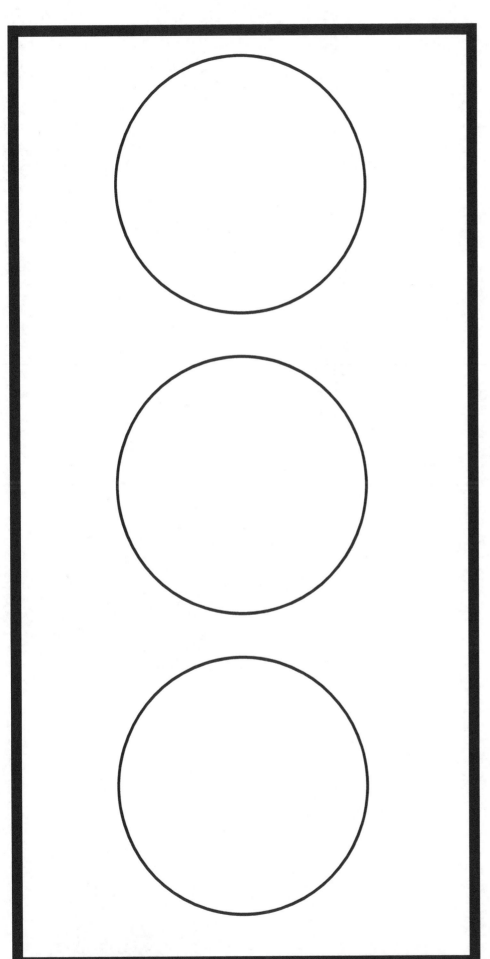

Color the rectangle black.
Cut the rectangle out.
Glue the circles from
the next page onto the
rectangle to make the
traffic light.

Color one circle red. Color one circle yellow. Color one circle green. Cut the circles out and glue them to the rectangle from the other page to make the traffic light.

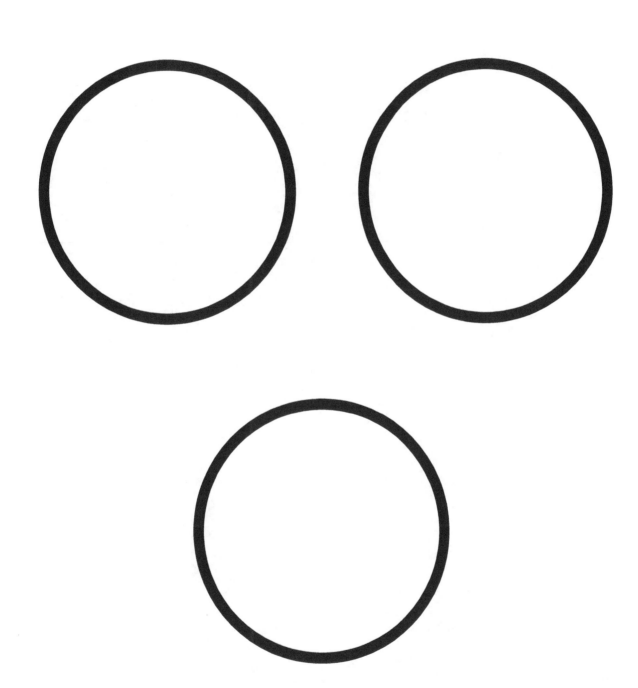

Cut out the items on the worksheet and glue them to construction paper as illustrated by the sample. Draw in the arms, legs, and face for the 0 manna man. Draw in the rest of the picture.

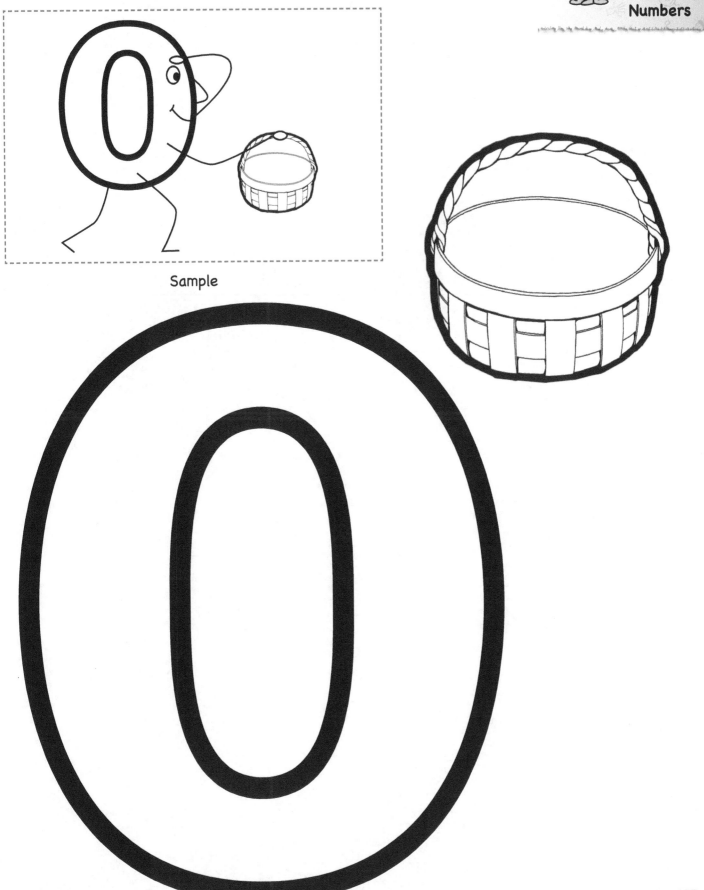

Sample

Draw a gray rectangle around the Mm letters, a purple circle around the Nn letters, and a green X on the Oo letters.

L   O   m   n

O   N   M   K

n   O   d   N

M   m   M   D

N   o   n   O

Count each group. Circle the correct number under each group.

6   7   8

7   8   9

0   1   2

5   6   7

1   2   3

3   4   5

Trace the rectangles. Count the rectangles in each drawing. Draw lines to connect pictures that look the same. You may color the pictures as you like.

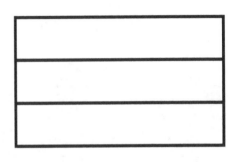

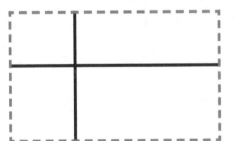

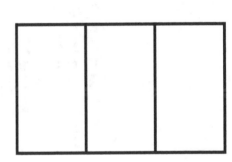

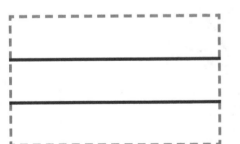

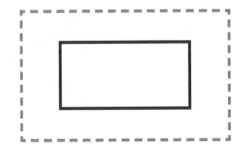

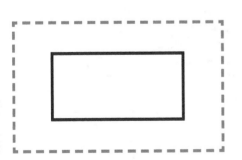

Color the tree house.

Trace the letters O and o with your finger. Can you see the letters Oo at the beginning of the words ostrich, octopus, otter, ox, and opossum?

Aa Bb Cc Dd Ee Ff Gg Hh Ii Jj Kk Ll

Mm

Nn

 Oo

Pp

Qq

Rr

Ss

Tt

Uu

Vv

Ww

Xx

Yy

Zz

O o

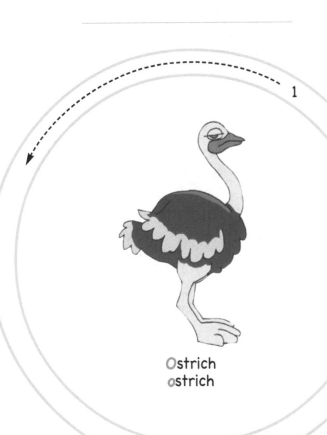

Ostrich
ostrich

Octopus
octopus

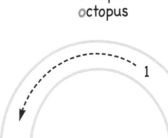

Otter
otter

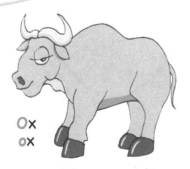

Ox
ox

Opossum
opossum

Lesson 49 Math

Connect the dots 0 to 9 to complete the drawing. Color the drawing.

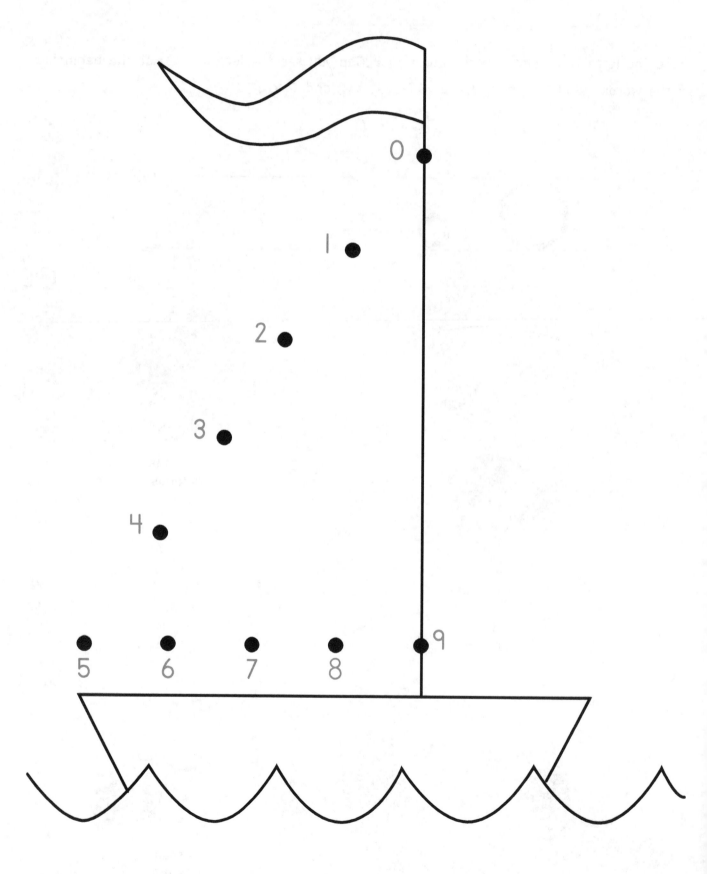

Students: Every time that you eat a meal, think about what you are eating. If you are eating part of a plant, write it in the space provided.

Parents: The students are learning about plants and how much we are dependent on them. Please help them fill in their chart and return it to class in ONE WEEK.

Sun	Mon	Tues	Wed	Thur	Fri	Sat
Breakfast	Breakfast	Breakfast	Breakfast	Breakfast	Breakfast	Breakfast
Lunch	Lunch	Lunch	Lunch	Lunch	Lunch	Lunch
Dinner	Dinner	Dinner	Dinner	Dinner	Dinner	Dinner

Examples: Cereal, vegetables, fruit, potatoes, peanut butter, jam, fruit roll ups, fruit juice, pizza (sauce), noodles, bread, cake (flour), cookies (flour), potato & corn chips

Trace the letters P and p with your finger. Can you see the letters Pp at the beginning of the words parakeet, penguin, prairie dog, porpoise, and porcupine?

Parakeet
parakeet

Porpoise
porpoise

Penguin
penguin

Prairie Dog
prairie dog

Parasaurolophus
parasaurolophus

Porcupine
porcupine

Lesson 50 Math

Trace the numbers. Count each group of items and draw a line to the correct number.

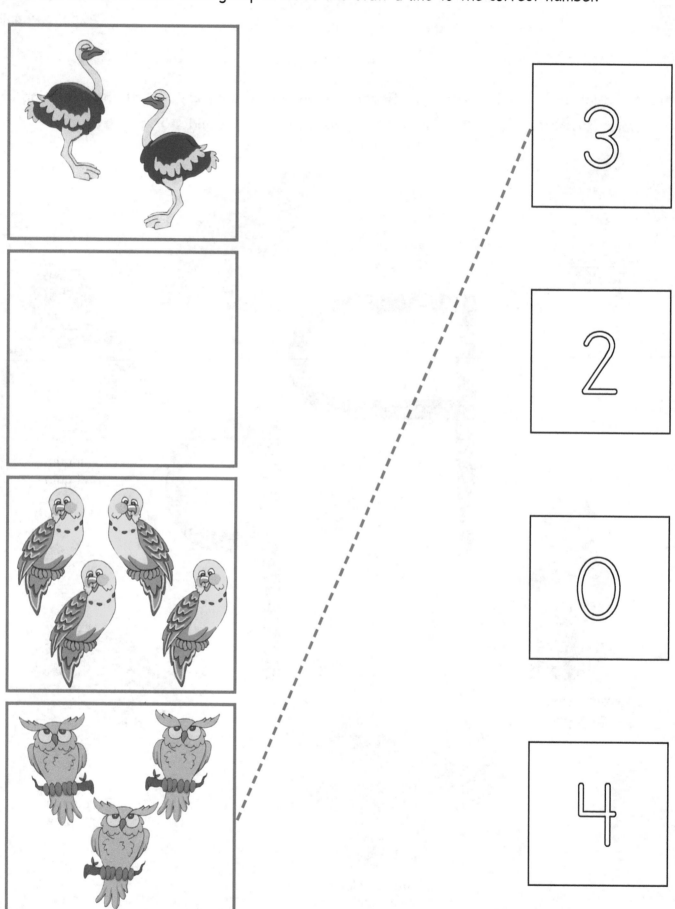

Draw lines to connect the shapes that are the same. You may color the pictures as you like.

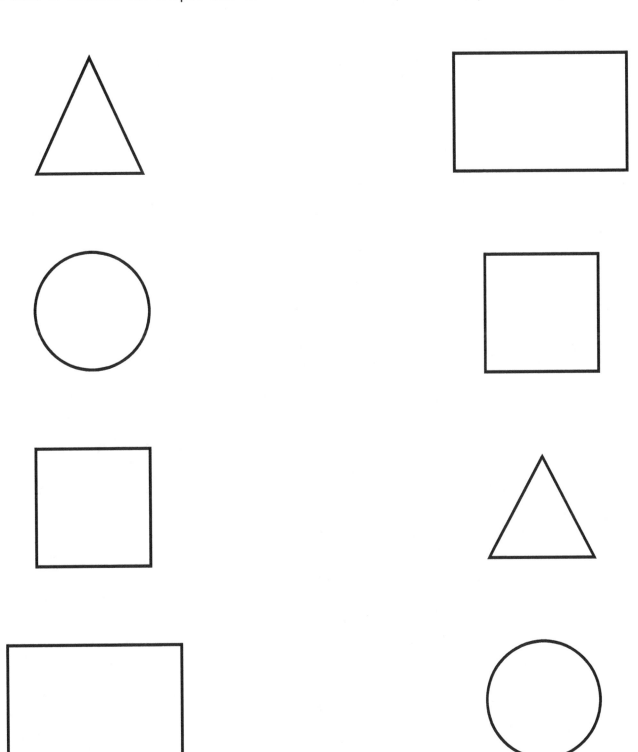

Color the parts of the turkey. Glue the page to a sheet of card stock or a piece of light brown construction paper. Cut out the parts of the turkey and glue them to a pine cone.

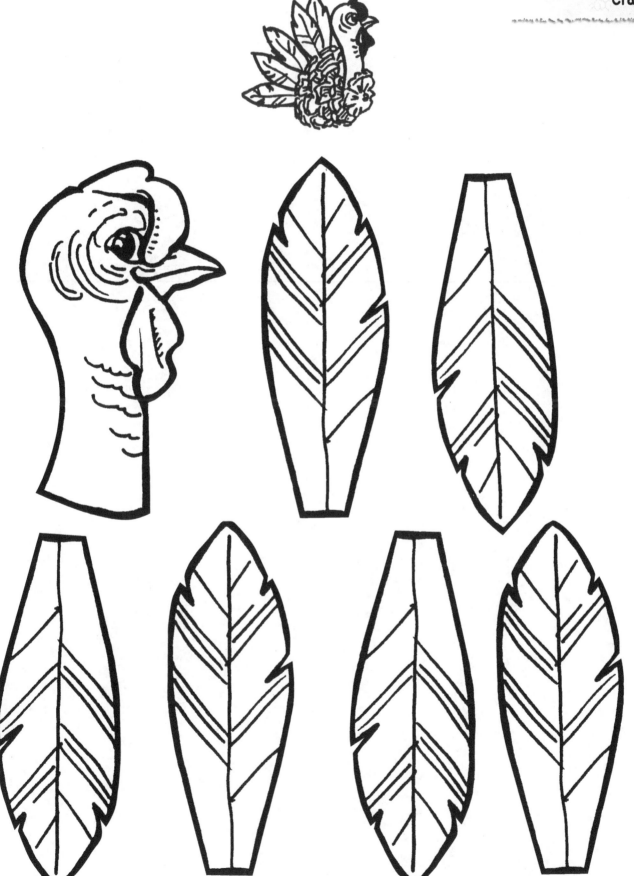

212

Use your finger to trace the large number 10. Count the animals and use a pencil to trace the numbers on the lines.

0   1   2   3   4   5   6   7   8   9   10   11   12

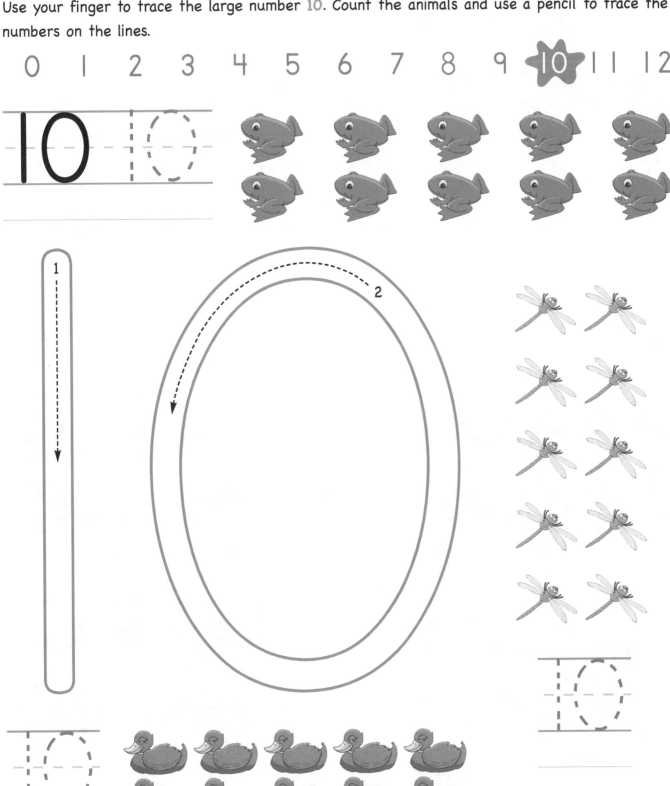

Lesson 51b Math

Count each group. Draw a line to the group that matches.

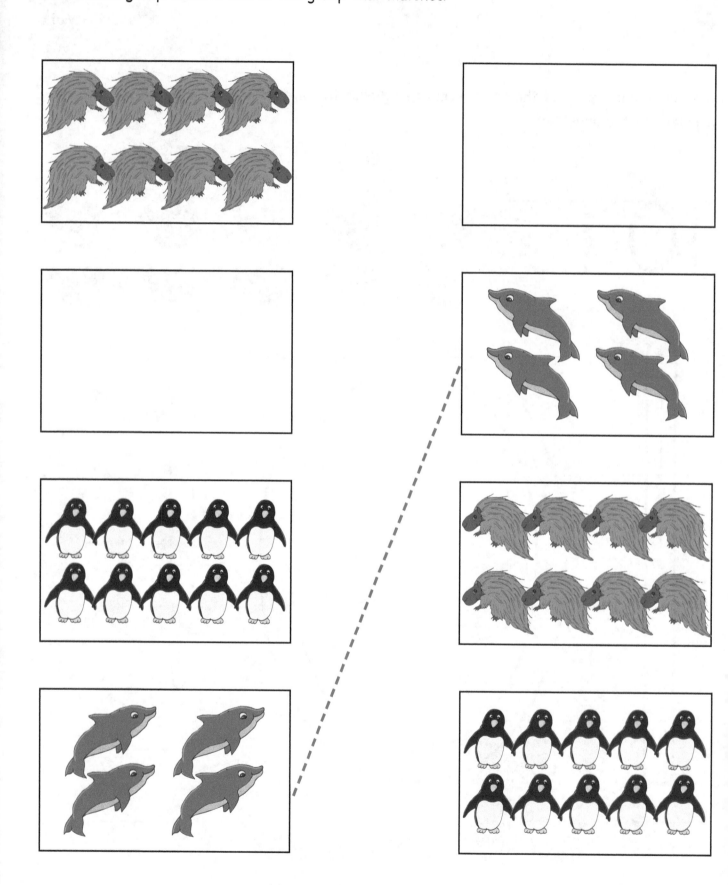

Draw a line between the shapes that are the same.

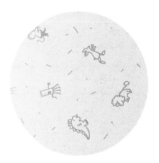

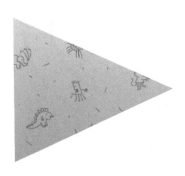

Trace the letters P and p with your finger. Can you see the letters Pp at the beginning of the words panda, pig, and polar bear?

Aa Bb Cc Dd Ee Ff Gg Hh Ii Jj Kk Ll

Mm

Nn

Oo

Pp

Qq

Rr

Ss

Tt

Uu

Vv

Ww

Xx

Yy

Zz

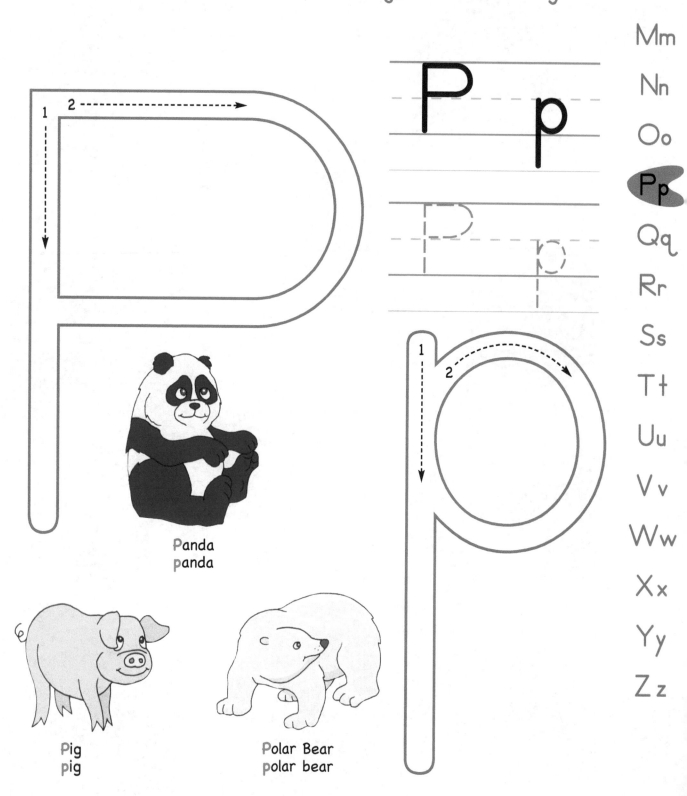

Panda
panda

Pig
pig

Polar Bear
polar bear

Cut out the number strip. Count each group and paste the correct number in each box.

 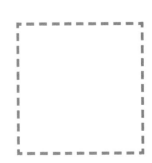

 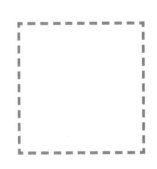

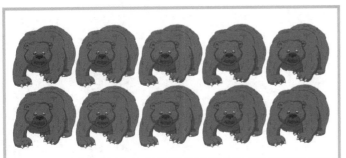 

0 5 9 10

217

Cut out the items on the worksheet and glue them to construction paper as illustrated by the sample. Draw in the arms, legs, and faces for the 10 girls. Draw in the rest of the picture.

Sample

Trace the letters Q and q with your finger. Can you see the letters Qq at the beginning of the words quail, quetzal, quagga, and quokka?

Quail
quail

Quetzal
quetzal

Quagga
quagga

Quokka
quokka

Lesson 53 Math

Count the animals in each group and then circle the correct number.

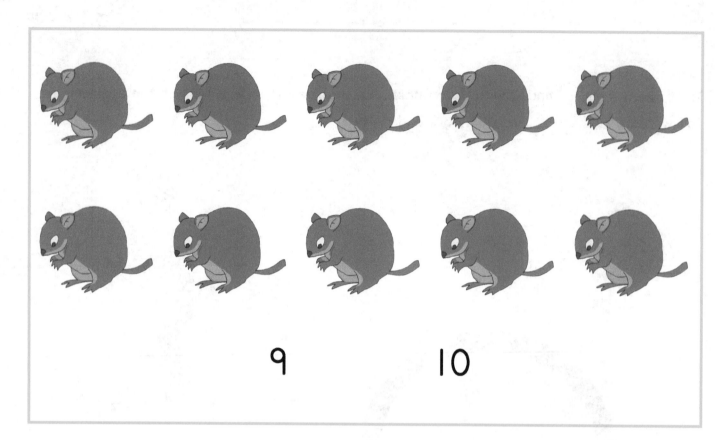

9   10

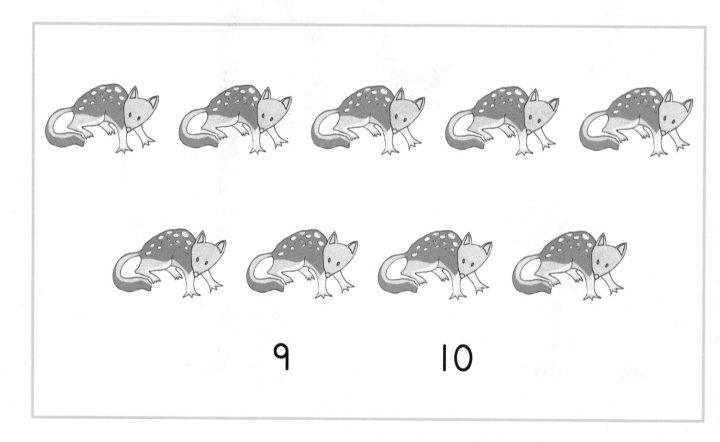

9   10

Trace each of the shapes, cut them out, and paste them on a sheet of paper in order of big, bigger, and biggest.

Trace the letters Q and q with your finger. Can you see the letters Qq at the beginning of the words quagga, quoll, quiver, and quokka?

Aa Bb Cc Dd Ee Ff Gg Hh Ii Jj Kk Ll
Mm
Nn
Oo
Pp
Qq
Rr
Ss
Tt
Uu
Vv
Ww
Xx
Yy
Zz

Q q

Quoll
quoll

Quagga
quagga

Quiver
quiver

Quokka
quokka

225

Count each group. Draw a line to the correct number.

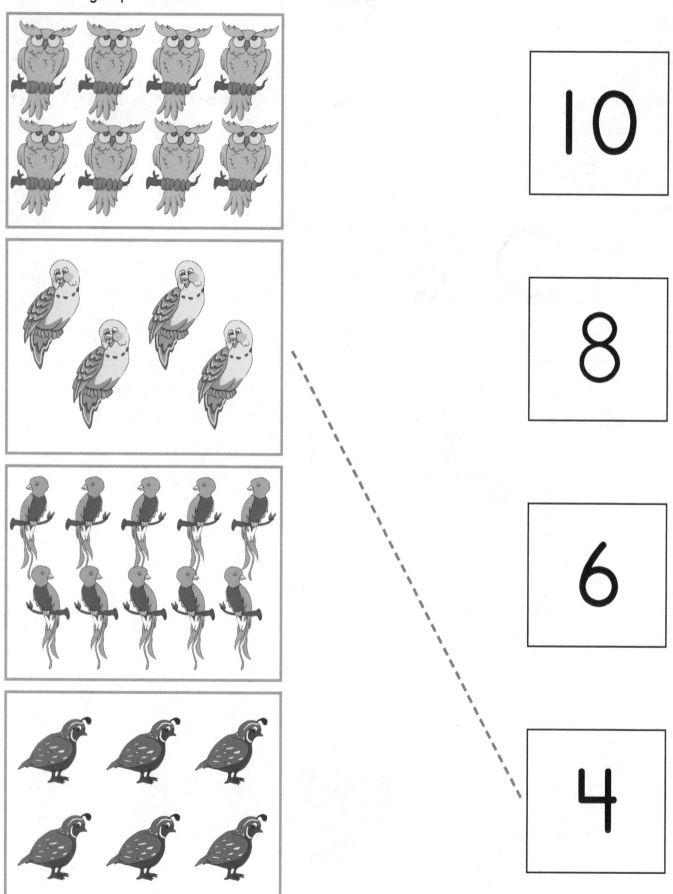

Find the circle, square, and dotted lines on the worksheet.
Cut from the circle to the square, following the dotted lines as closely
as you can.

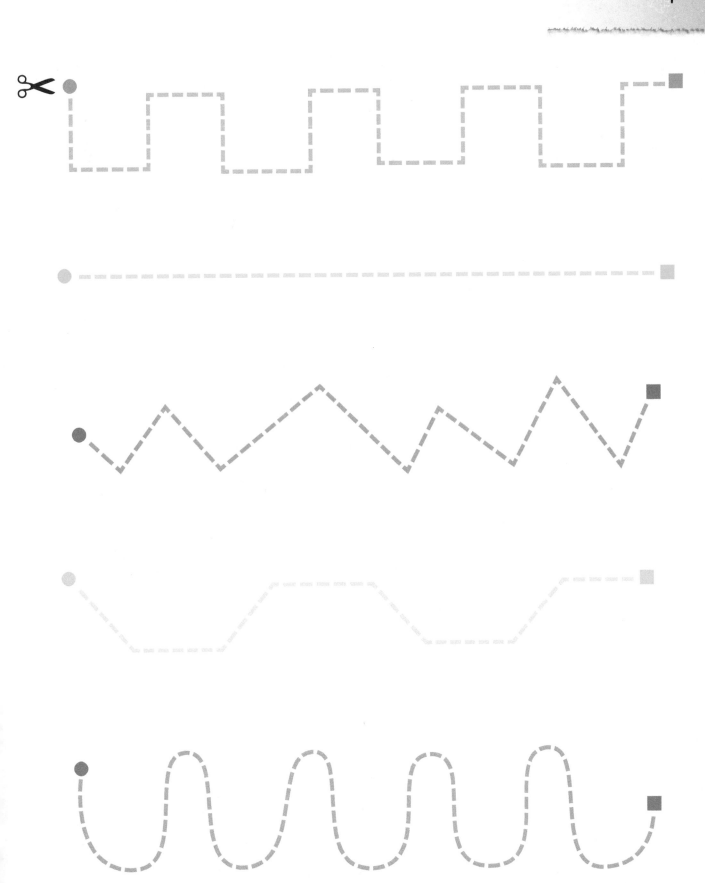

227

Students: Today you have learned a lot about cotton. Take this paper to your room. Look in your closet and in your dresser drawers. See if you have any items made of 100% cotton. Draw their picture on this paper and return it to school tomorrow.

Parents: Help your student with this assignment.

Draw an orange square around the Pp letters and a blue circle around the Qq letters.

P   p   Q   q

p   N   q   K

n   P   d   Q

p   q   P   Q

N   q   n   p

Trace the numbers. Count each group of items and draw a line to the correct number.

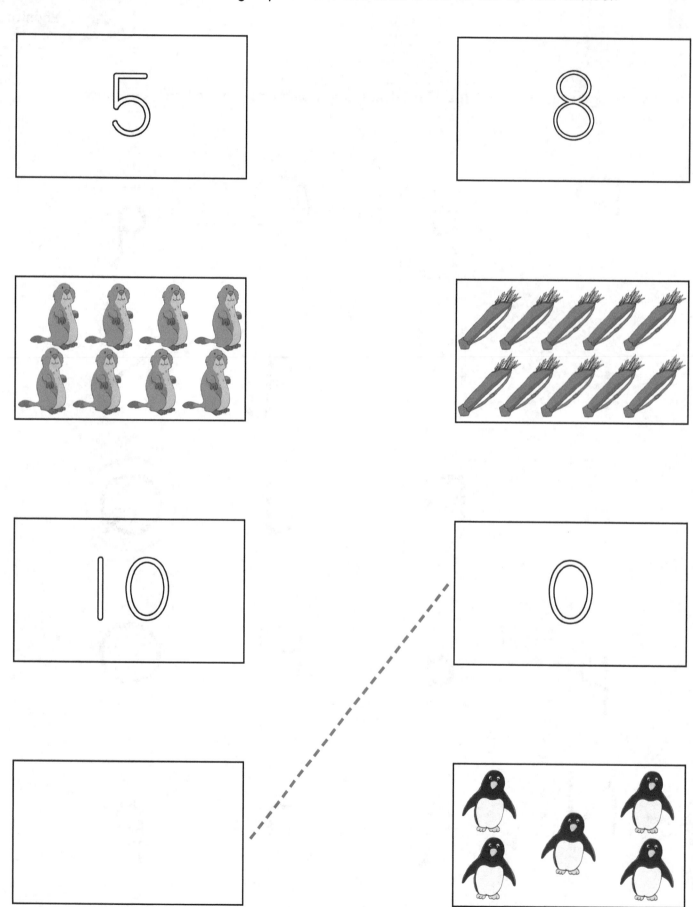

Trace the letters R and r with your finger. Can you see the letters Rr at the beginning of the words rabbit, raccoon, rattlesnake, reindeer, and rhino?

Rabbit
rabbit

Raccoon
raccoon

Reindeer
reindeer

Rattlesnake
rattlesnake

Rhino
rhino

Count and color the correct number of boxes in each strip. The first one is done for you.

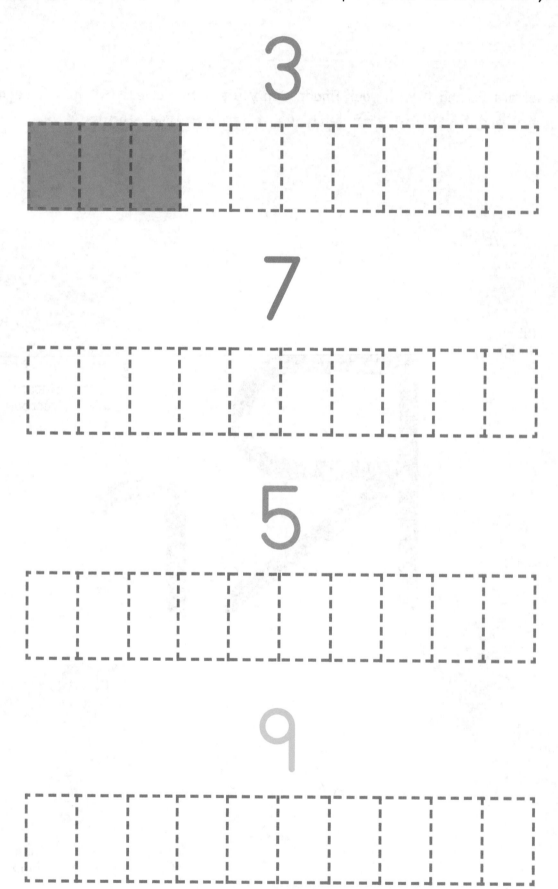

Count the triangles and the rectangles. Count the triangles and rectangles altogether. Trace the triangles and rectangles on the dotted lines. Color the shapes. Cut out the shapes and paste them on another sheet of paper to make the sailboat.

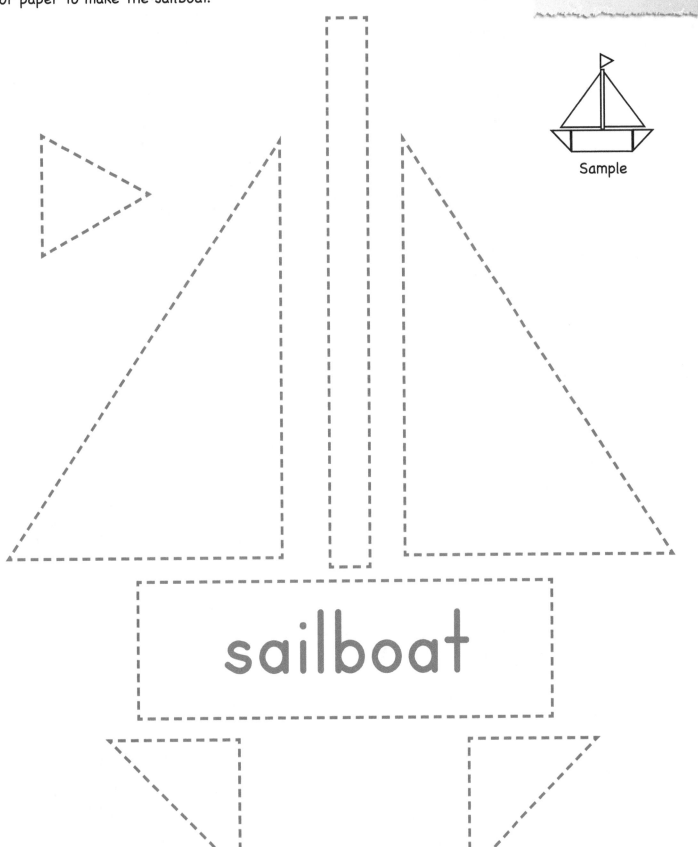

Sample

235

Count the dots in each tile and draw a line to the correct number.

10

5

7

4

Students: This is a month-long assignment. Every morning look outside and see what the weather is like. In each square draw a sun, a cloud, or some rain.

Parents: Please help your student make a calendar of this page. Just write in numbers to make four weeks of time. Keep the homework page near the breakfast area and help the student to remember to fill in the days with the weather.

Sun	Mon	Tues	Wed	Thur	Fri	Sat

Count and color to fill in the Snake Path from start to finish. Use the Color Key and color in order the number of steps listed.

Color Key

1 = red

2 = green

3 = blue

1 = black

2 = yellow

3 = brown

2 = pink

3 = purple

2 = orange

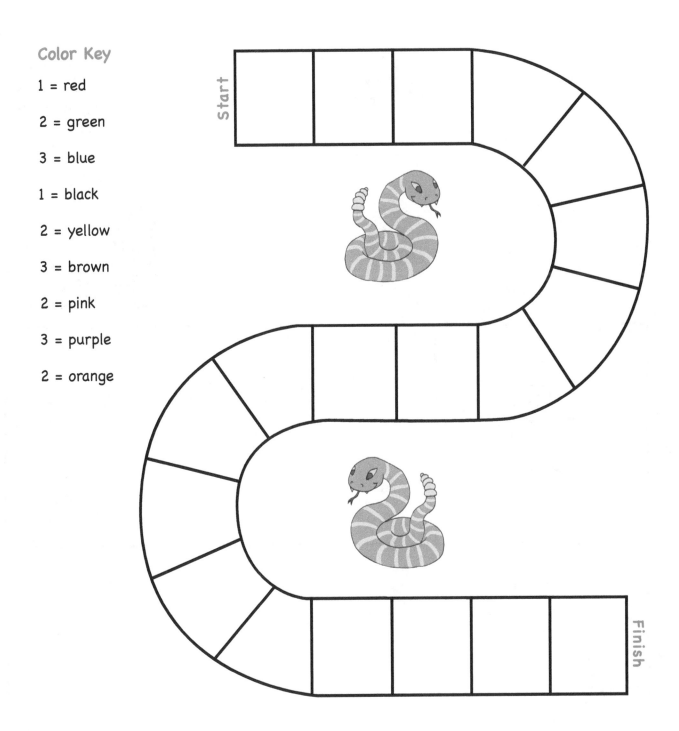

Lesson 58 Shapes

Trace the star. You may color the star. Color the flag of Chile to match the sample.

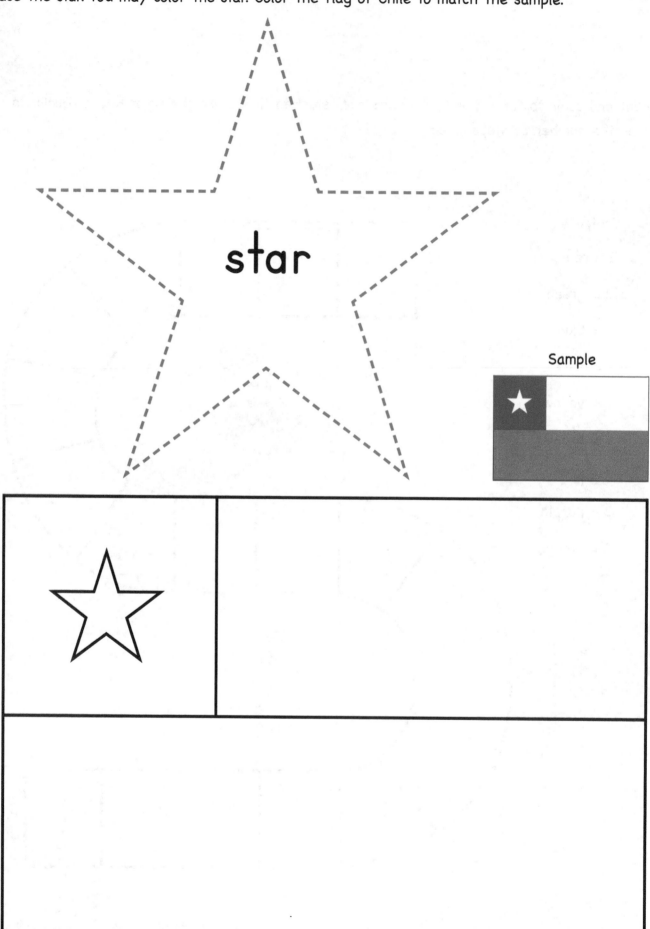

star

Sample

Cut on the dotted line. Cut out the clock hands. Poke a little hole in the clock and the two hands with a pencil point. Using a brad, attach the clock's little/short hand to the clock. Save the big/longer hand for later. The pattern can be glued to card stock for a sturdier clock.

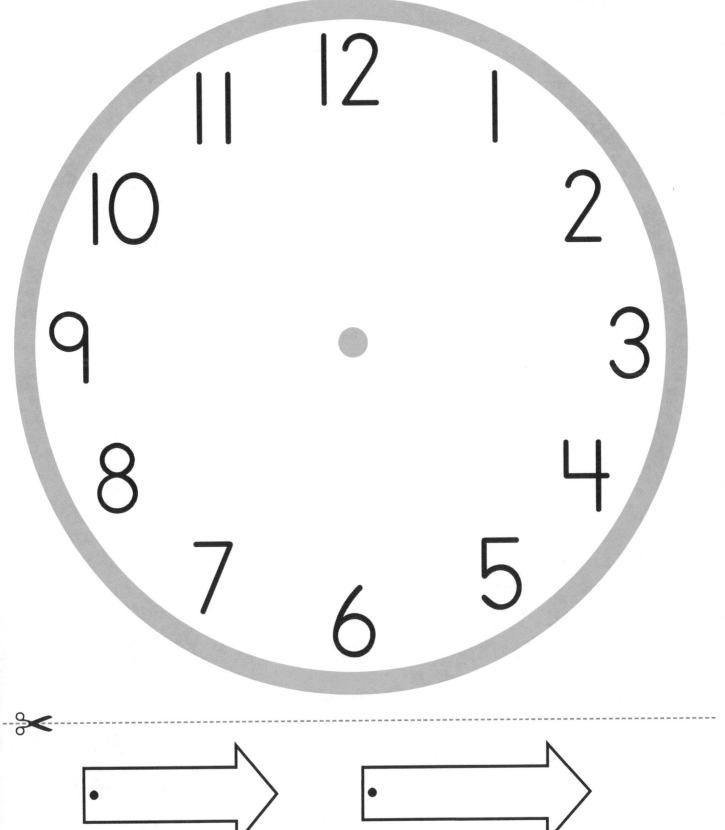

Trace the letters R and r with your finger. Can you see the letters Rr at the beginning of the words roadrunner, robin, rooster, and rabbit?

Aa Bb Cc Dd Ee Ff Gg Hh Ii Jj Kk Ll

Mm

Nn

Oo

Pp

Qq

Rr

Ss

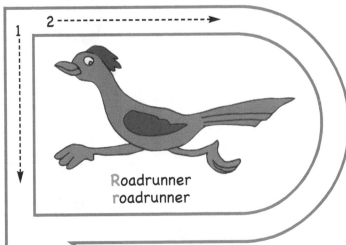

Roadrunner
roadrunner

Robin
robin

Tt

Uu

Vv

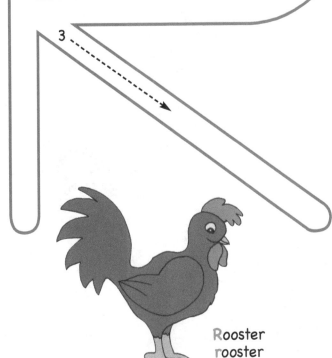

Rooster
rooster

Rabbit
rabbit

Ww

Xx

Yy

Zz

Count the dots on each tile and draw a line to match it to the correct number.

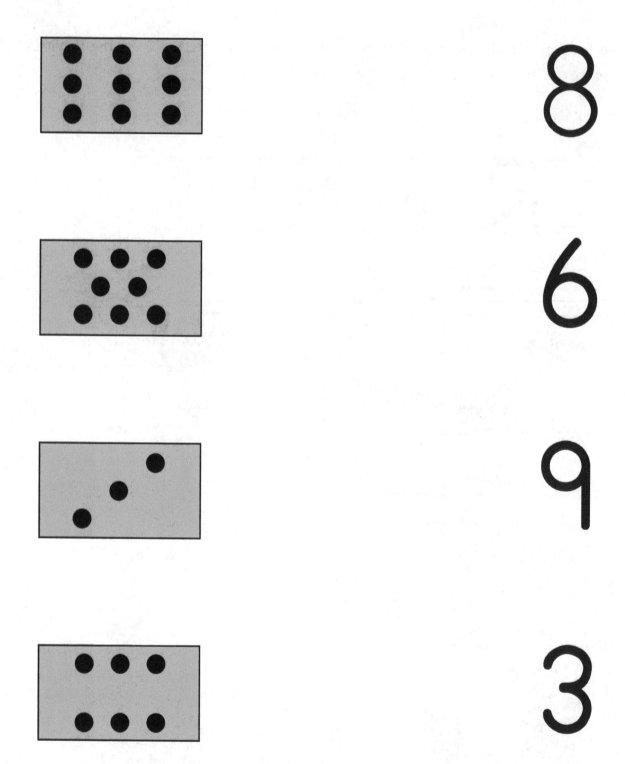

Trace the circle. Trace the letters in the word circle. Look for the letter r in the word.
You may color the circle.

circle

circle

Lesson 60 Language Arts

Trace the lines to match the items for the same season.

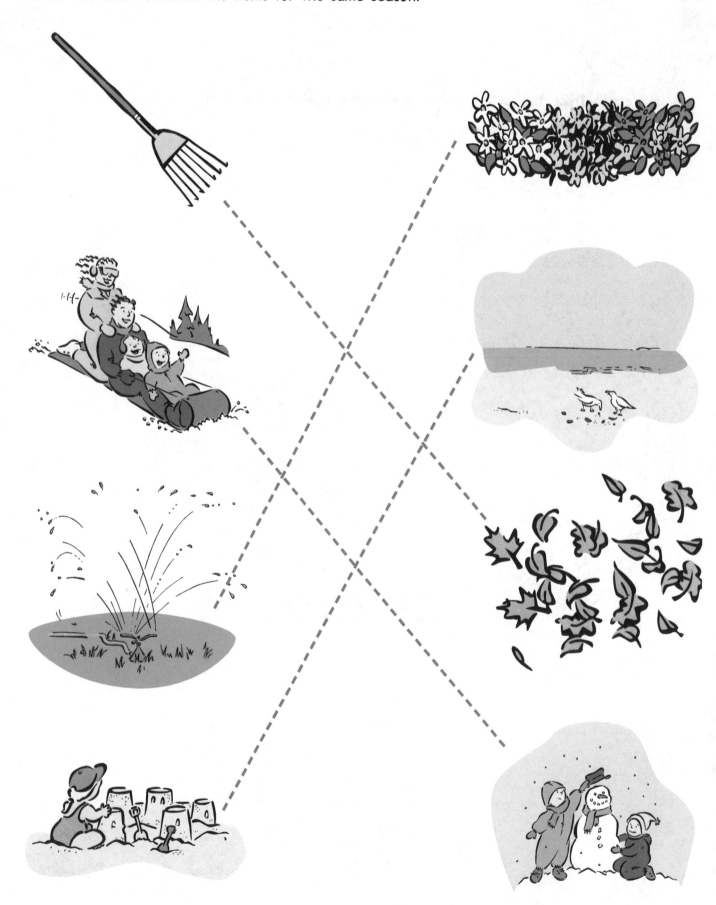

Trace the letters S and s with your finger. Can you see the letters Ss at the beginning of the words skunk, squirrel, scorpion, starfish, and spider?

Sauropod
sauropod

Squirrel
squirrel

Scorpion
scorpion

Starfish
starfish

Spider
spider

249

Count the dots on each tile and trace the number.

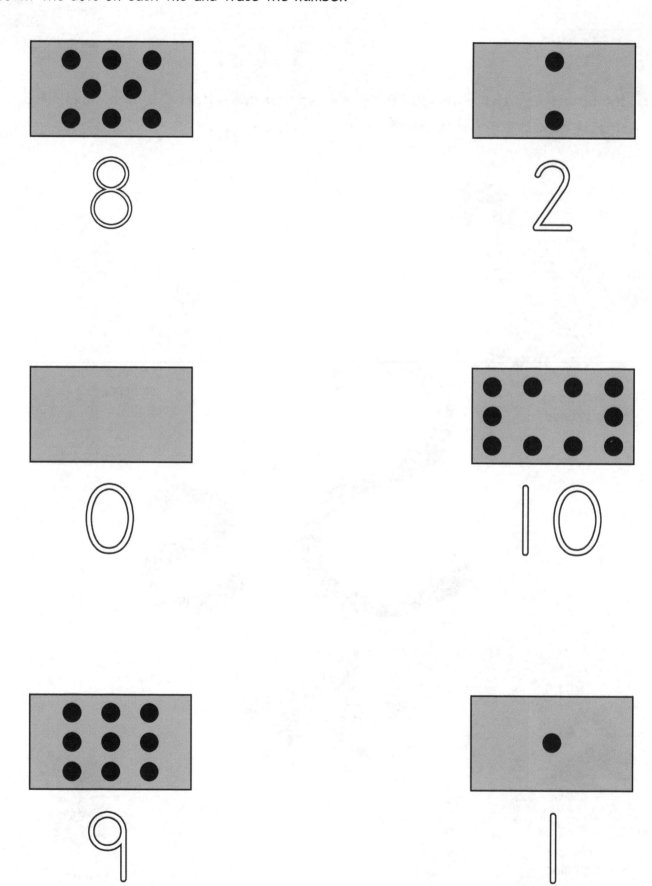

Draw a circle around the clothes that are worn in the summer.

Lesson 61 Math

Count the groups of items one at a time and draw a line to the number.

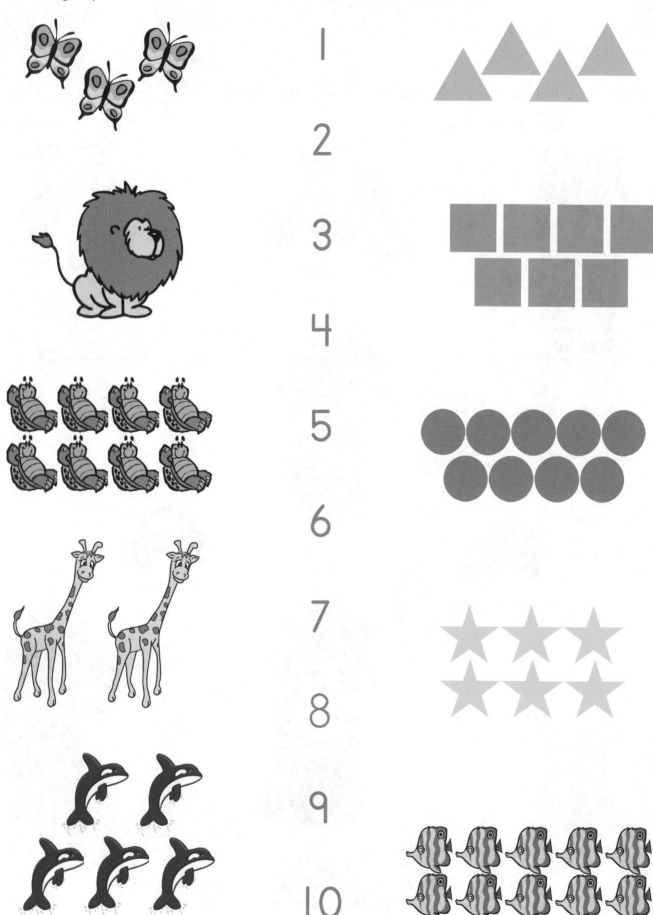

1

2

3

4

5

6

7

8

9

10

Find the numbers on the ball and color the spaces the color listed.

Color by number.

Color spaces with number **1** yellow.

Color spaces with number **3** blue.

Color spaces with number **2** red.

Color spaces with number **4** green.

Color spaces with number **5** your favorite color!

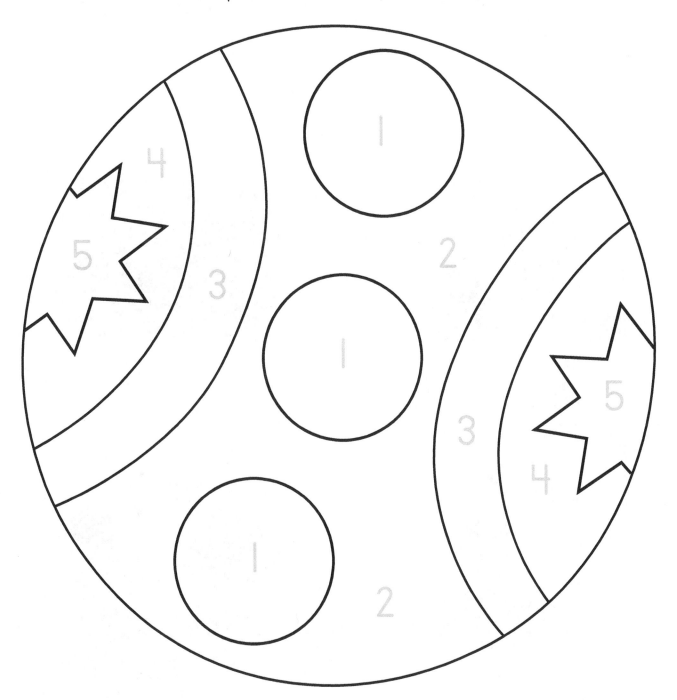

Lesson 62 Language Arts

Draw a circle around things that happen in the summer.

Trace the letters S and s with your finger. Can you see the letters Ss at the beginning of the words seal, shark, sheep, squirrel, and skunk?

Aa Bb Cc Dd Ee Ff Gg Hh Ii Jj Kk Ll

Mm

Nn

S s   S s

Oo

Pp

Qq

Rr

Ss

Tt

Uu

Vv

Ww

Xx

Yy

Zz

Seal
seal

Shark
shark

Sheep
sheep

Squirrel
squirrel

Skunk
skunk

255

Lesson 62 Memory Verse

Trace the word "wisdom" inside the heart, then color the rest of the drawing as you wish.

Draw a circle around the clothes that are worn in the fall.

Trace the letters T and t with your finger. Can you see the letters Tt at the beginning of the words toucan, toad, tamarin, tiger, timber wolf, and turtle?

Toucan
toucan

Toad
toad

Tamarin
tamarin

Tiger
tiger

Triceratops
triceratops

Timber Wolf
timber wolf

Count and color the correct number of boxes in each strip.

Lesson 63 Shapes

Count the number of points on the starfish. Color the starfish.

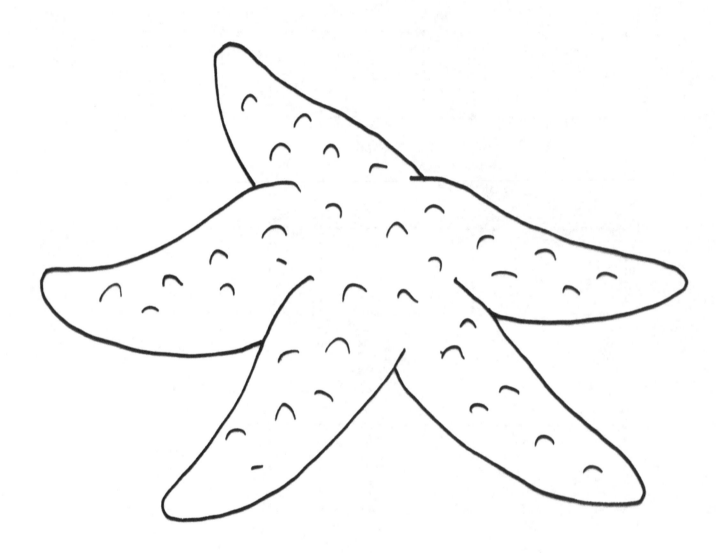

Trace the letters T and t with your finger. Can you see the letters Tt at the beginning of the words turkey, tarantula, trout, and t-rex?

Aa Bb Cc Dd Ee Ff Gg Hh Ii Jj Kk Ll
Mm
Nn
Oo
Pp
Qq
Rr
Ss
Tt
Uu
Vv
Ww
Xx
Yy
Zz

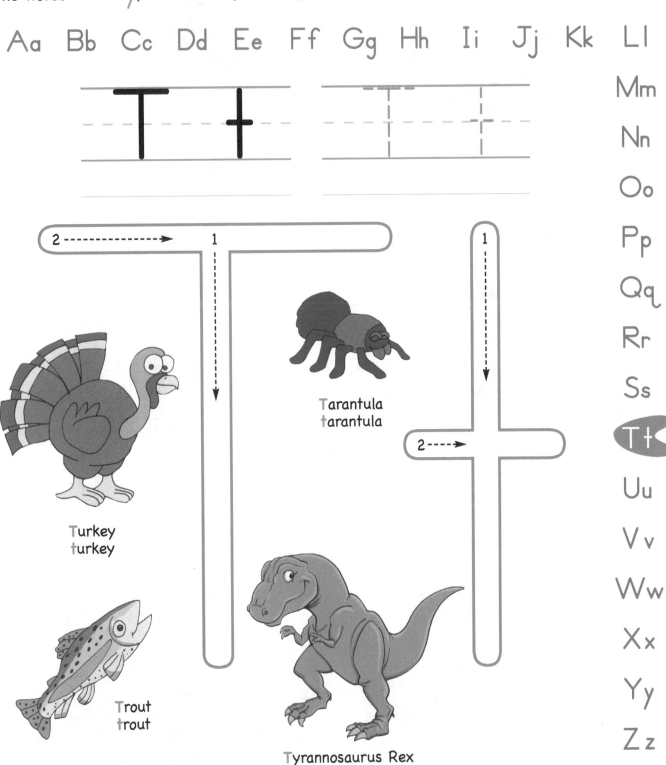

Turkey
turkey

Tarantula
tarantula

Trout
trout

Tyrannosaurus Rex
tyrannosaurus rex

261

Lesson 64 Language Arts

Draw a circle around the things that happen in the fall.

Read the number. Draw the correct number of objects for each number.

Counting Practice

Numbers   Things to count:

1	
2	
3	
4	
5	
6	
7	
8	
9	
10	

Lesson 64 Shapes

Begin with letter A. Connect the dots in alphabet order to make the picture. Color the drawing.

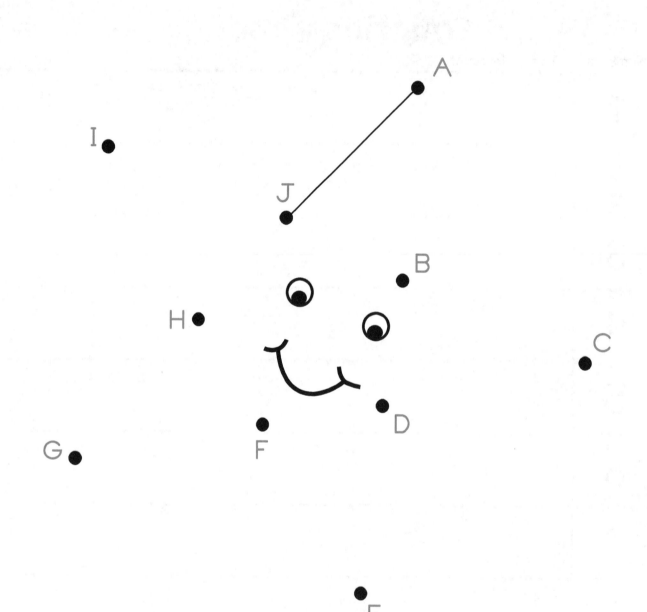

Draw a circle around the clothes that are worn in the winter.

Draw a blue star around the Rr letters, a brown rectangle around the Ss letters, and a yellow X on the Tt letters.

Connect the dots 1 to 10 to complete the picture. You may color the drawing.

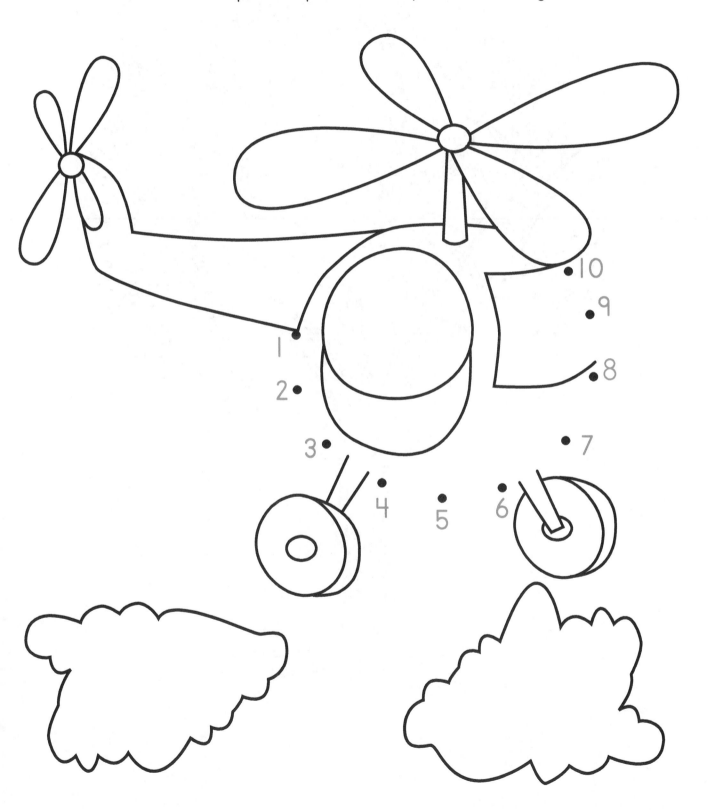

Lesson 65 Science

Draw a winter scene with the tree.

Draw a circle around the clothes that are worn in the spring.

Trace the letters U and u with your finger. Can you see the letters Uu at the beginning of the words umbrella, umbrella bird, unicycle, and urchin?

Umbrella
umbrella

Umbrella Bird
umbrella bird

Unicycle
unicycle

Urchin
urchin

Look at the patterns in each row. Circle the shape that would come next in the pattern.

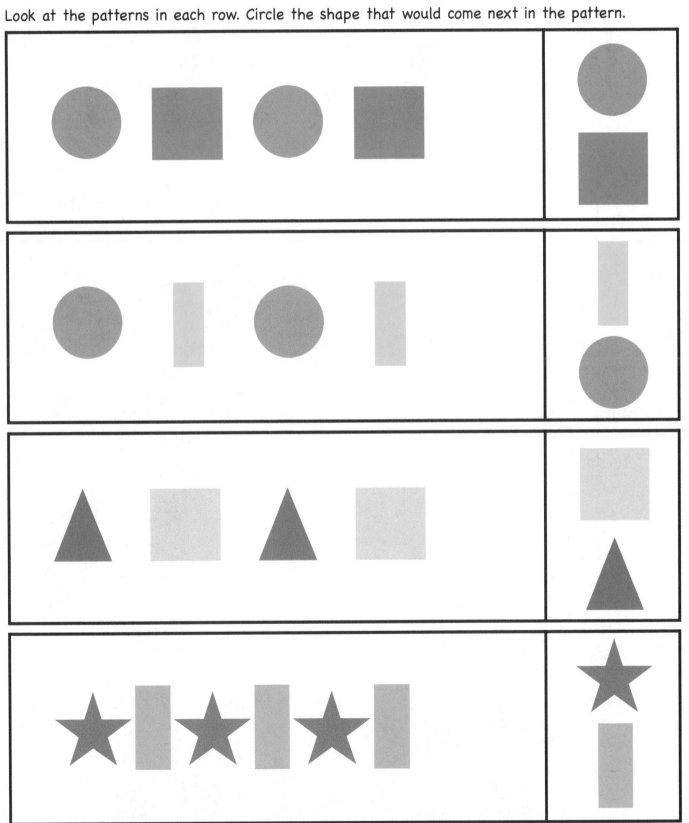

Use your finger to trace the large number 11. Count the animals and use a pencil to trace the numbers on the lines.

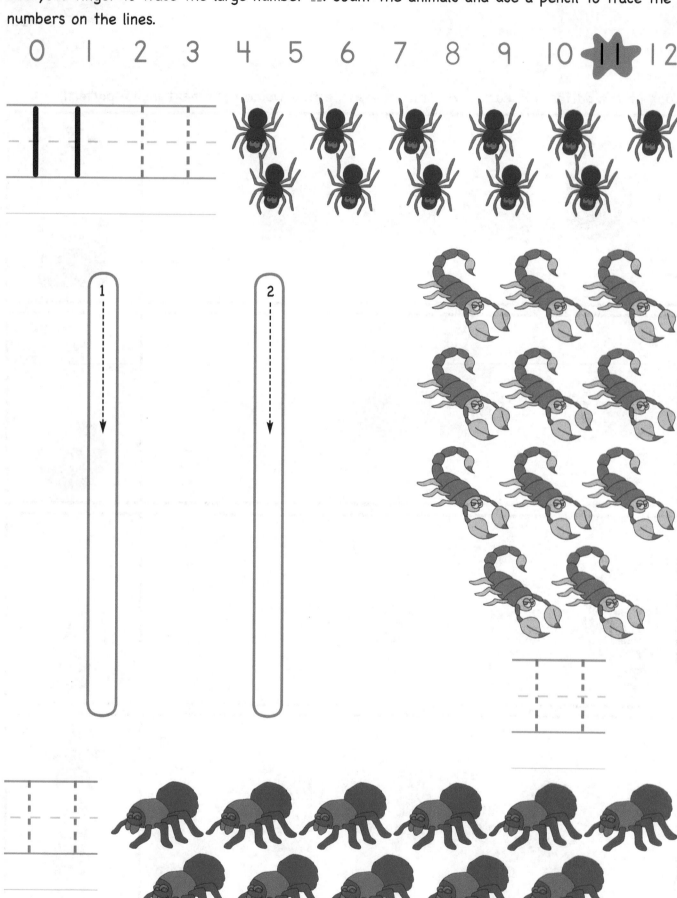

Count each group. Draw a line to the group that matches.

Lesson 66 Memory Verse

Color the sections of the umbrella as you learn your memory verse. Use the colors purple, blue, green, yellow, orange, and red.

Draw a circle around the things that happen in the winter.

Trace the letters U and u with your finger. Can you see the letters Uu at the beginning of the words umbrella cockatoo, unicorn, unicycle, and urchin?

Aa Bb Cc Dd Ee Ff Gg Hh Ii Jj Kk Ll
Mm
Nn
Oo
Pp
Qq
Rr
Ss
Tt
Uu
Vv
Ww
Xx
Yy
Zz

U u

1

Umbrella Cockatoo
umbrella cockatoo

Unicorn
unicorn

1   2

Unicycle
unicycle

Urchin
urchin

277

Lesson 67 Math

Trace the numbers. Count each group of items and draw a line to the correct number.

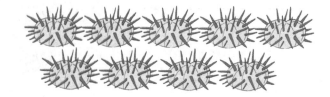

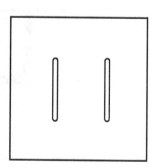

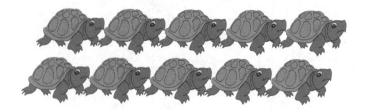

Cut out the items on the worksheet and glue them to construction paper as illustrated by the sample. Draw in the arms, legs, and faces for the 11 that is watching the stars bow down. Draw in the rest of the picture.

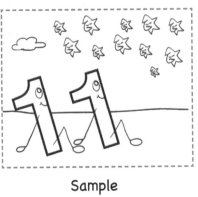

Sample

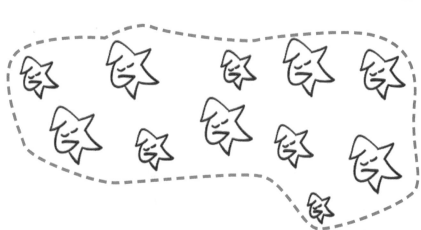

Draw a circle around the things that happen in the spring.

Lesson 68 Math

Connect the dots. Color the picture.

Trace the shapes, name them, and color the drawings.

Trace the lines to match items from the same season.

Look at the patterns in each row. Circle the shape that would come next in the pattern.

Count the dots on each tile and match it to the correct number.

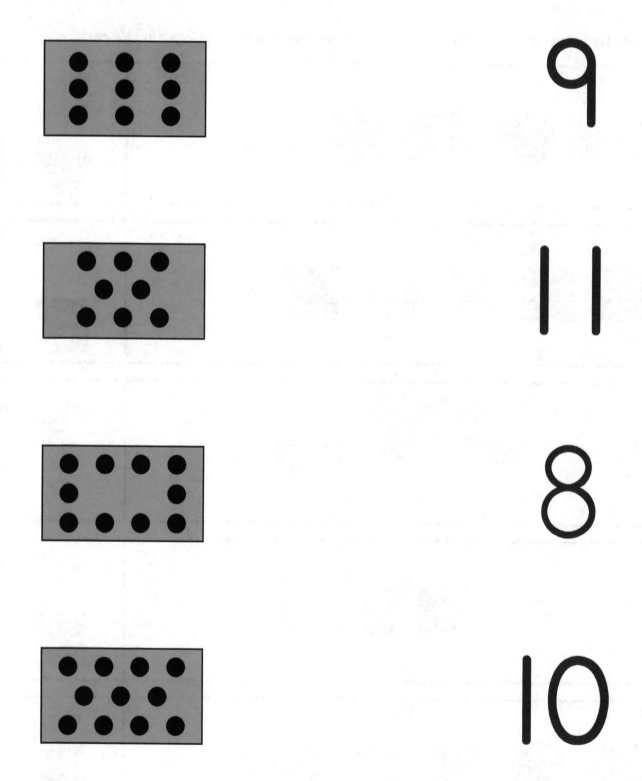

Students: Share with your family what you learned today. Explain what "STOP, DROP, ROLL" means. Practice with your family.

Parents: The old "STOP, DROP, ROLL" that you memorized years ago is still very important. Encourage your child by practicing this with them.

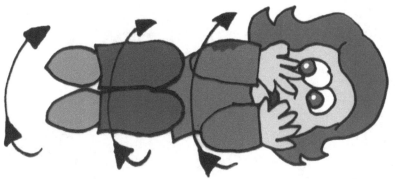

288

Trace the letters V and v with your finger. Can you see the letters Vv at the beginning of the words violet, volcano, vulture, and vampire bat?

Violet
violet

Volcano
volcano

Vulture
vulture

Vampire Bat
vampire bat

Trace the numbers. Count each group of items and draw a line to the correct number.

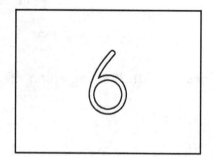

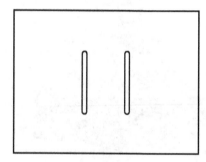

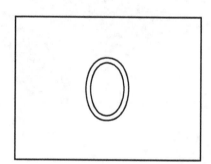

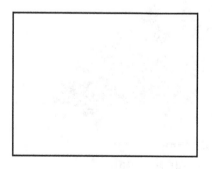

Use your finger to trace the large number **12**. Count the items and use a pencil to trace the numbers on the lines.

0   1   2   3   4   5   6   7   8   9   10   11   **12**

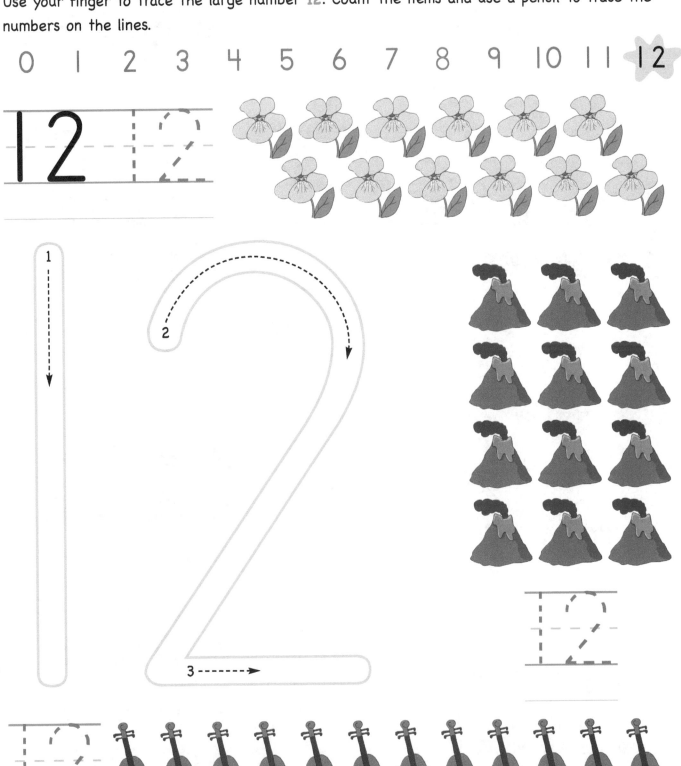

Lesson 71b Math

Count each group. Draw a line to the group that matches.

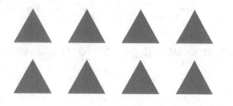

Trace the letters V and v with your finger. Can you see the letters Vv at the beginning of the words vole, vulture, vampire bat, and viper?

Aa Bb Cc Dd Ee Ff Gg Hh Ii Jj Kk Ll
Mm
Nn
Oo
Pp
Qq
Rr
Ss
Tt
Uu
Vv
Ww
Xx
Yy
Zz

V v   V v

Vole
vole

Vulture
vulture

Vampire Bat
vampire bat

Viper
viper

293

Cut out the number strip. Count each group and paste the correct number in each box.

| 0 | 5 | 9 | 10 |

Cut out the items on the worksheet and glue them to construction paper as illustrated by the sample. Draw in the arms, legs, and faces for the 12 that is gathering the baskets of leftovers. Draw in the rest of the picture.

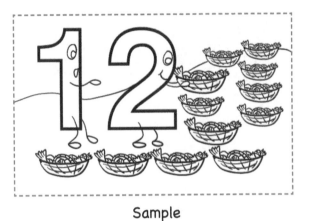

Sample

Trace the letters W and w with your finger. Can you see the letters Ww at the beginning of the words weasel, warthog, wolf, woodpecker, whale, and walrus?

Weasel
weasel

Warthog
warthog

Wolf
wolf

Woodpecker
woodpecker

Whale
whale

Walrus
walrus

Count each group. Circle the correct number under each group.

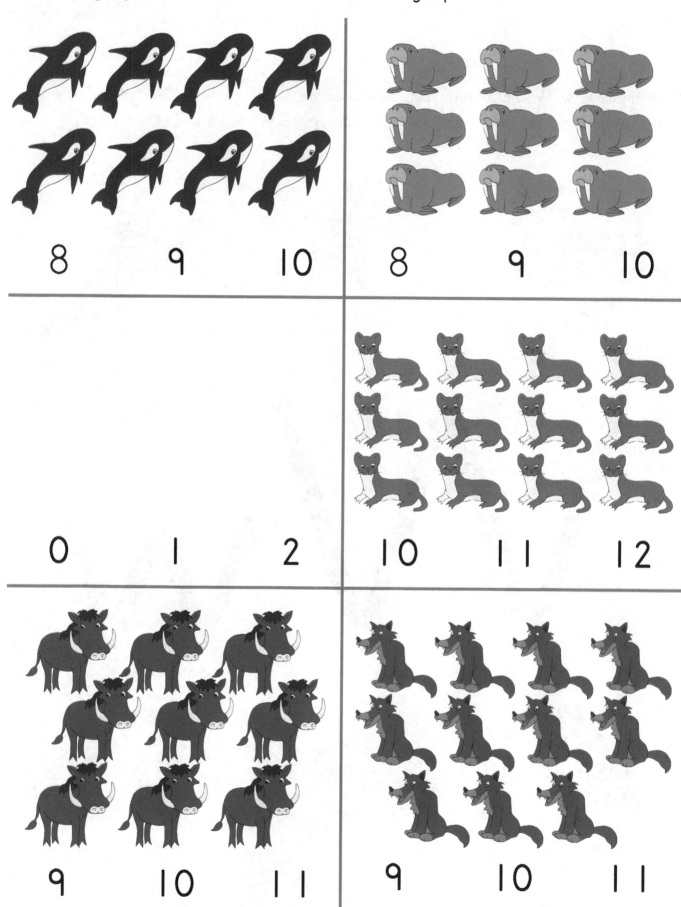

8   9   10

8   9   10

0   1   2

10   11   12

9   10   11

9   10   11

Trace the heart. Trace the letters in the word heart. You may color the heart.

heart

Lesson 74 Phonics

Trace the letters W and w with your finger. Can you see the letters Ww at the beginning of the words wolf, warthog, and wolverine?

Aa Bb Cc Dd Ee Ff Gg Hh Ii Jj Kk Ll
Mm
Nn
Oo
Pp
Qq
Rr
Ss
Tt
Uu
Vv
Ww
Xx
Yy
Zz

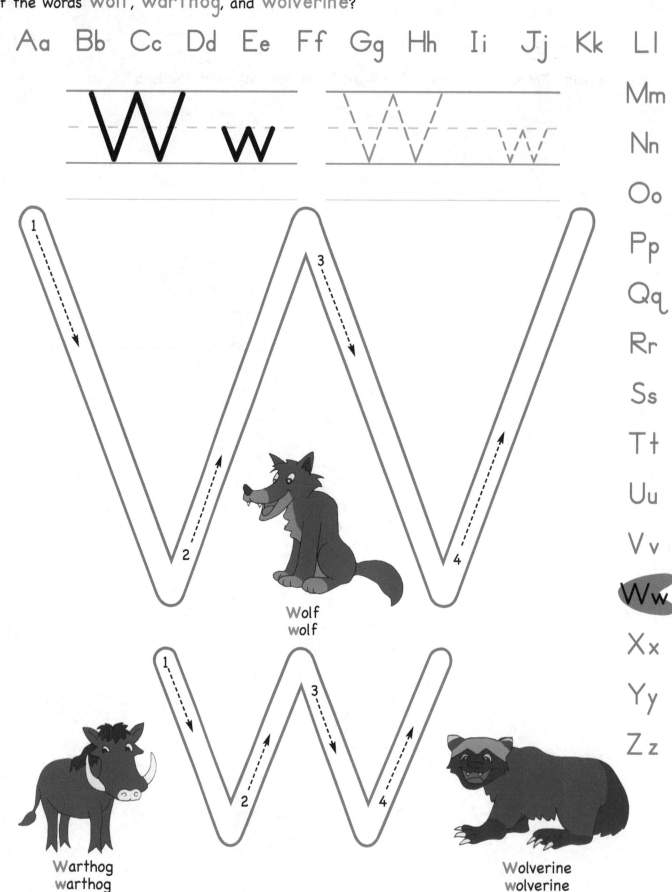

Wolf
wolf

Warthog
warthog

Wolverine
wolverine

Cut the pattern apart. Put the puzzle together in number order.

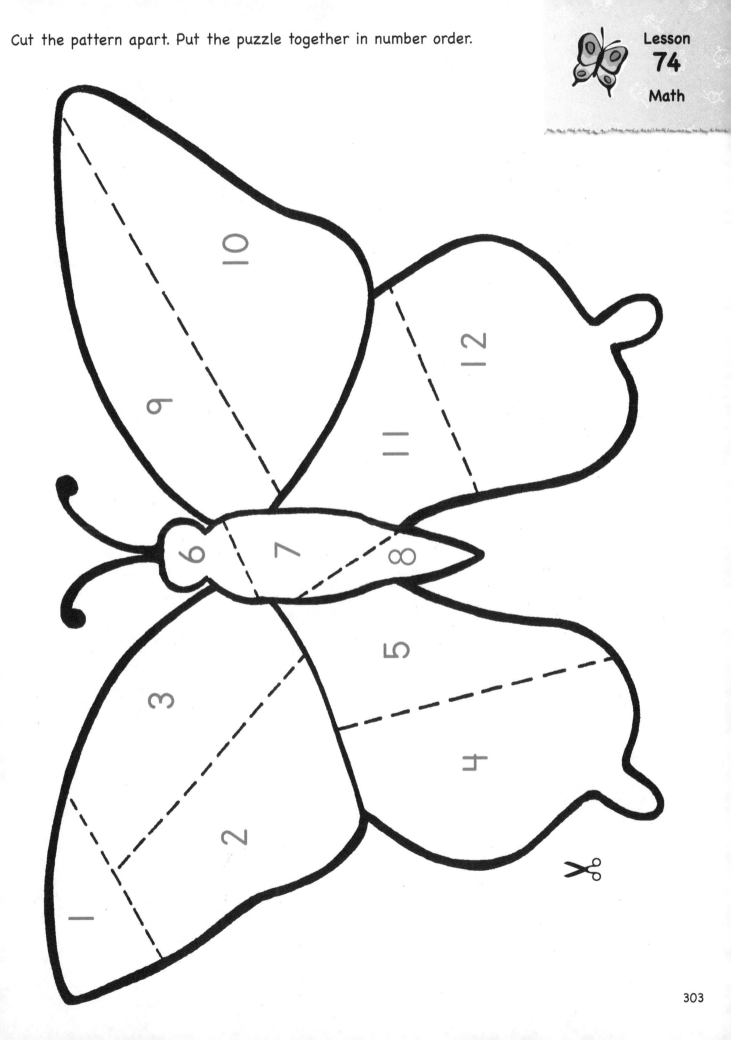

Draw a red heart around the Uu letters, a purple X on the Vv letters and a black circle around the Ww letters.

Lesson 75a Math

Look at the pattern in each large box. In the small box, circle the picture that would come next.

Optional: Make up your own pattern and draw it below. Ask your teacher or another student to circle the picture that comes next in your pattern.

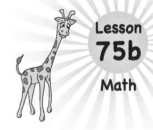

Trace the numbers. Count each group of items and draw a line to the correct number.

7

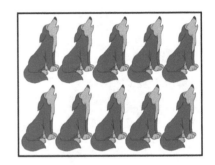

10

12

8

Trace the letters X and x with your finger. Can you see the letters Xx at the beginning of the words x-ray fish, x-ray, xenops, and xylophone?

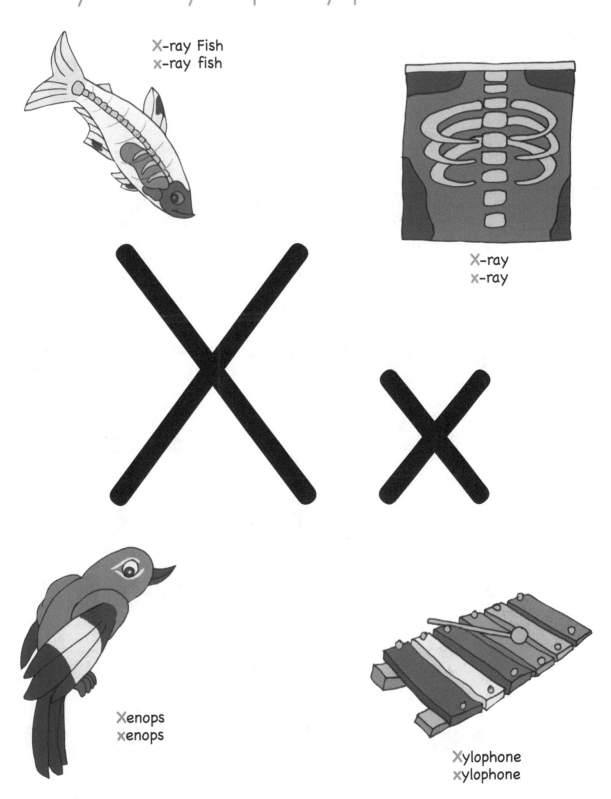

X-ray Fish
x-ray fish

X-ray
x-ray

Xenops
xenops

Xylophone
xylophone

Lesson 76 Math

Circle the correct number of objects for each number.

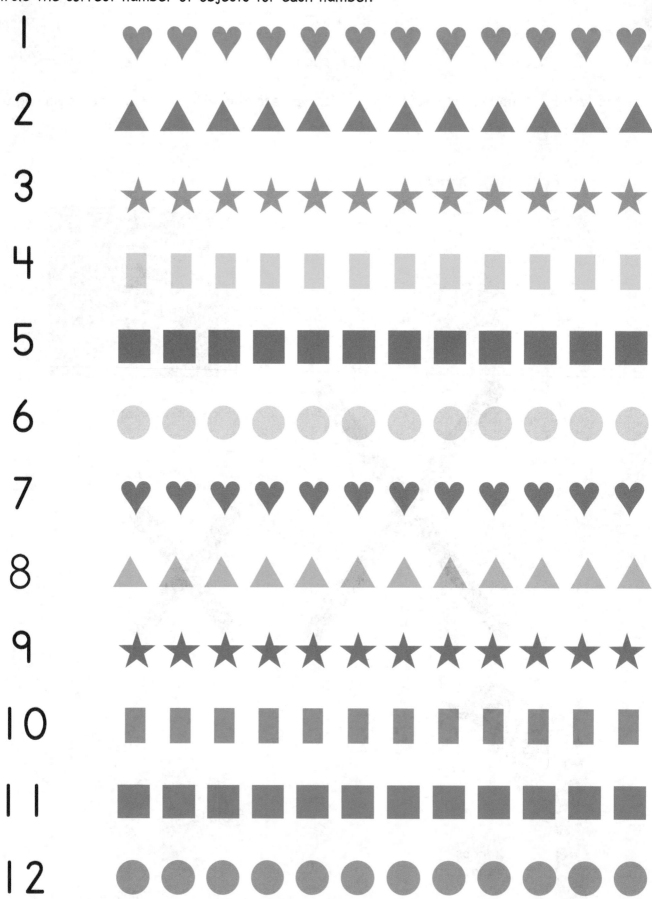

1

2

3

4

5

6

7

8

9

10

11

12

Trace the letters X and x with your finger. Can you see the letters Xx at the beginning of the words xenops and x-ray fish? Can you see the letter x at the end of the words fox and T-rex?

Aa Bb Cc Dd Ee Ff Gg Hh Ii Jj Kk Ll

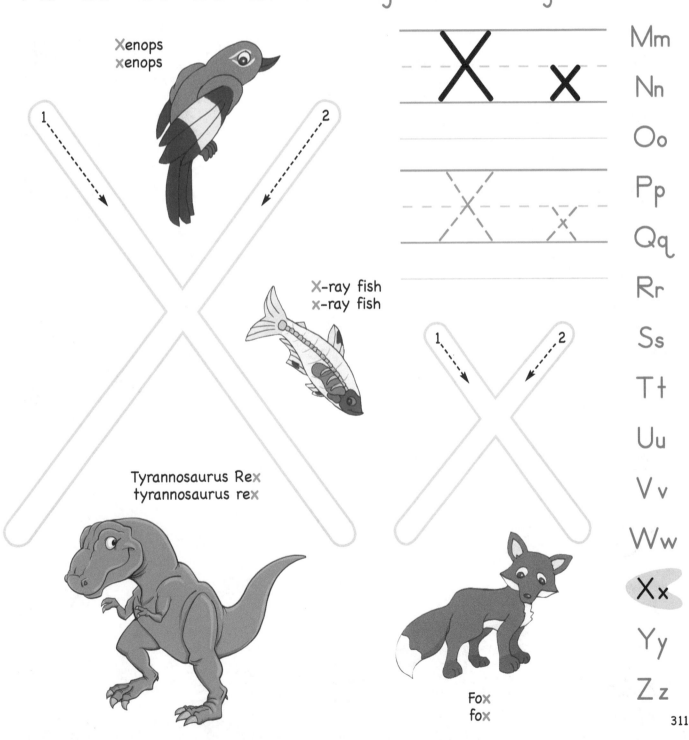

Xenops
xenops

X-ray fish
x-ray fish

Tyrannosaurus Rex
tyrannosaurus rex

Fox
fox

Mm

Nn

Oo

Pp

Qq

Rr

Ss

Tt

Uu

Vv

Ww

Xx

Yy

Zz

311

Draw lines to match the numbers.

0	0
1	6
2	4
3	8
4	10
5	9
6	3
7	12
8	5
9	11
10	2
11	1
12	7

(A line is drawn connecting 12 on the left to 12 on the right.)

Trace the letters Y and y with your finger. Can you see the letters Yy at the beginning of the words yarn, yoke, yacht, and yo-yo?

Yarn
yarn

Yoke
yoke

Yacht
yacht

Yo-yo
yo-yo

Count and color the correct number of boxes in each strip.

Follow the letters in alphabet order to help Smuggles find his way back to Nancy.

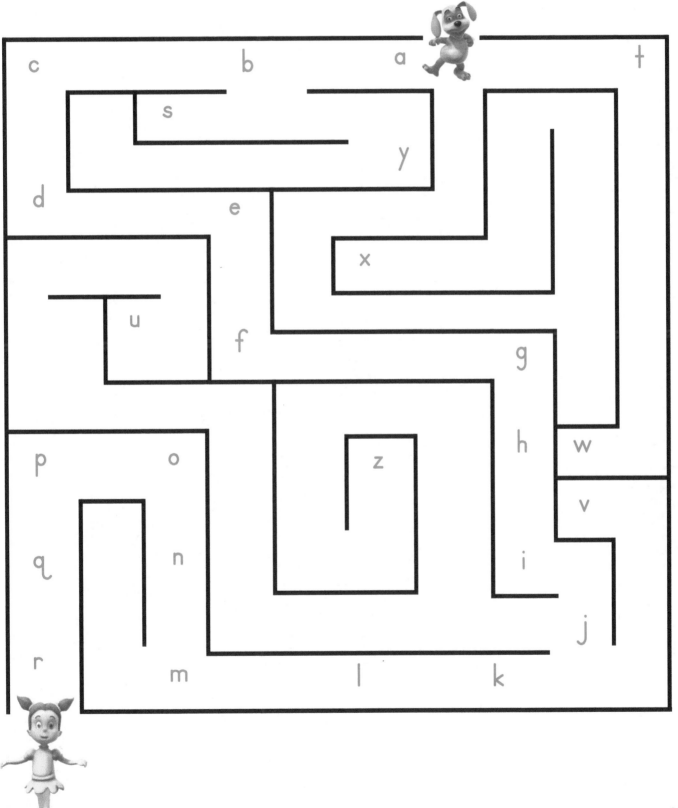

Color, paste the sheet on cardstock or construction paper, cut out, and punch the holes. Use yarn to tie the pieces to a coat hanger as illustrated in the sample.

sun

moon

Sample

sun

moon

Trace the letters Y and y with your finger. Can you see the letters Yy at the beginning of the words yolk, Yorkshire terrier, yak, and yellowjacket?

Aa Bb Cc Dd Ee Ff Gg Hh Ii Jj Kk Ll

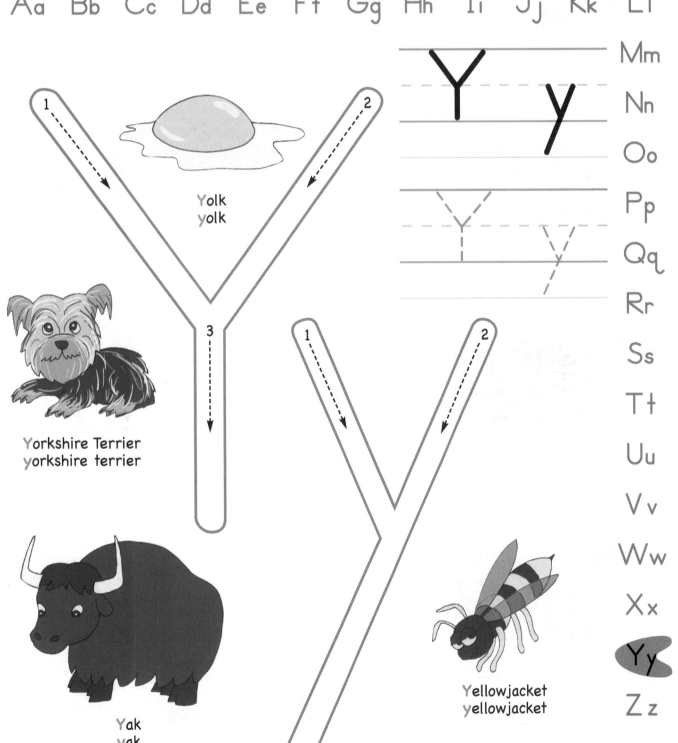

Mm

Nn

Oo

Pp

Qq

Rr

Ss

Tt

Uu

Vv

Ww

Xx

Yy

Zz

Yolk
yolk

Yorkshire Terrier
yorkshire terrier

Yak
yak

Yellowjacket
yellowjacket

Lesson 79 Math

Count the dots on each tile and draw a line to the number.

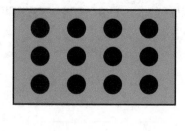

12

10

Students: You have been learning that God wants us to be **Shining Stars** for Him.
Think about the many ways you can be a **Shining Star for God**. Every time you do something special for your family or friends, you will receive a star to place in the night sky picture.

Parents: Purchase a package of silver star stickers. Encourage your student to be a **Shining Star for God**. When your child does something special for others, allow him to stick a star to the sky. Do this activity for a week. It doesn't need to be returned to class.

Place star stickers on the stars and trace the dotted lines to clarify the shape of the constellation.

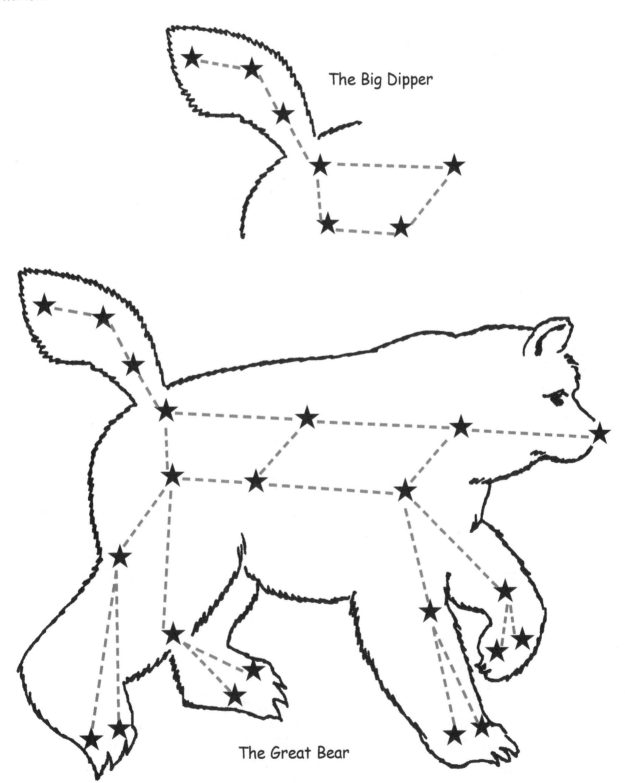

The Big Dipper

The Great Bear

Trace the letters Z and z with your finger. Can you see the letters Zz at the beginning of the words zorilla, zebra, zebu, and zorro?

Zorilla
zorilla

Zebra
zebra

Zebu
zebu

Zorro
zorro

325

Lesson 80b Phonics

Trace the letters Z and z with your finger. Can you see the letters Zz at the beginning of the words zinnia, zeppelin, zipper, and zucchini?

Aa Bb Cc Dd Ee Ff Gg Hh Ii Jj Kk Ll

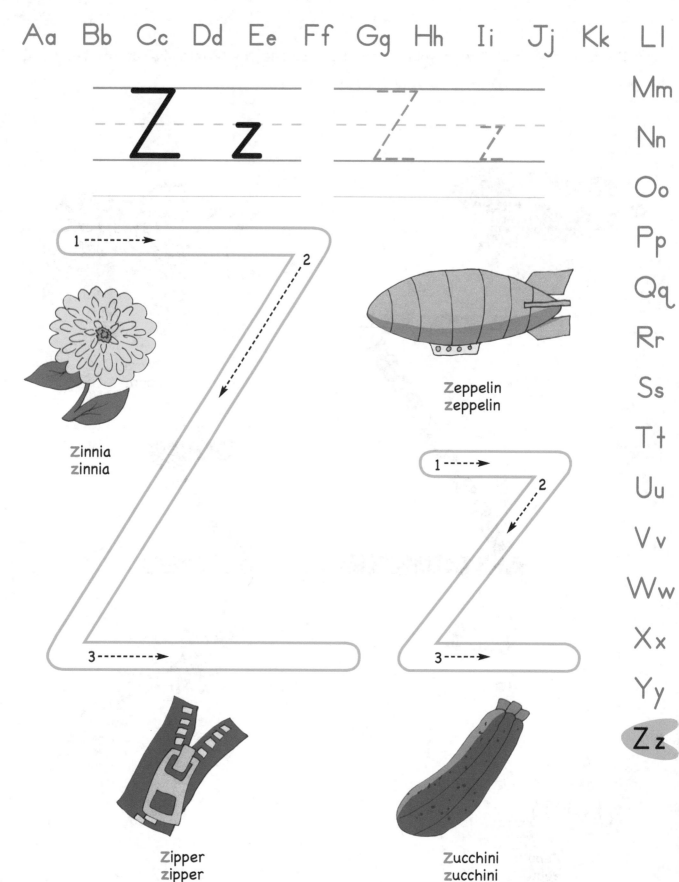

Mm

Nn

Oo

Pp

Qq

Rr

Ss

Tt

Uu

Vv

Ww

Xx

Yy

Zz

Zinnia
zinnia

Zeppelin
zeppelin

Zipper
zipper

Zucchini
zucchini

Trace the line as closely as you can to help the robin find the worm.

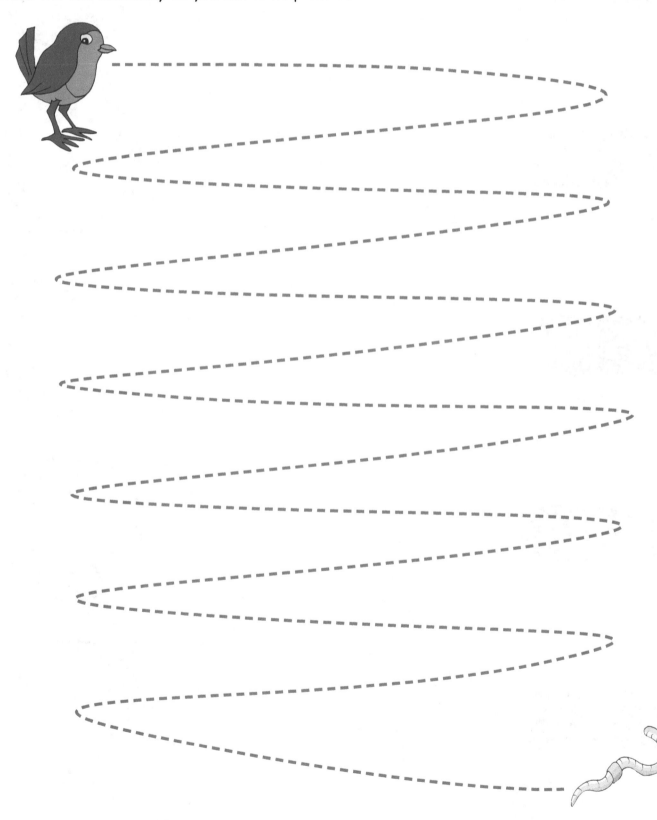

Lesson 81 Math

Draw a line to match the clocks that say the same time.

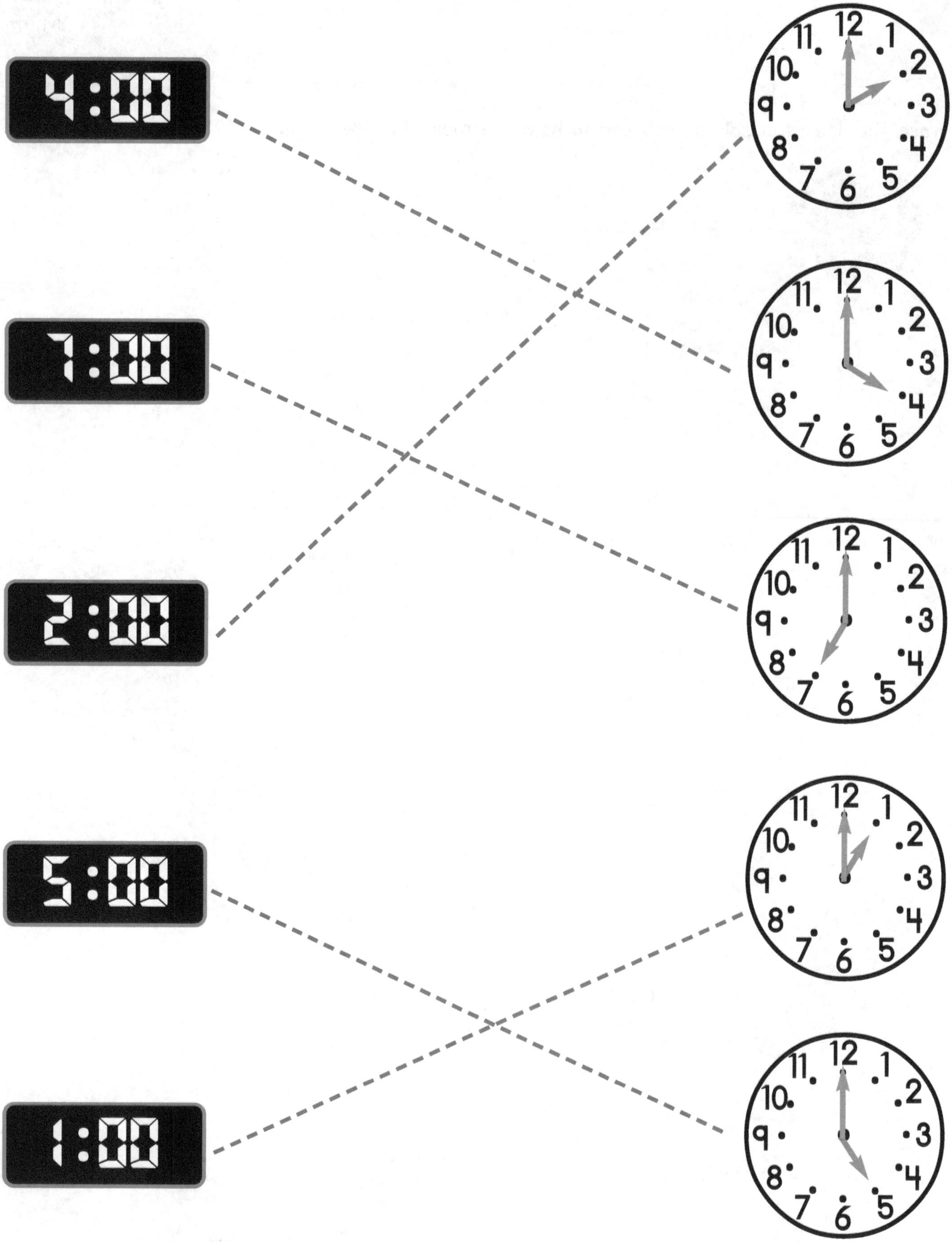

4:00

7:00

2:00

5:00

1:00

Each day you can say your memory verse you will get a star to paste on the picture.

Say the name of the letter. Say the sound of the letter. Trace the letters with your pencil.

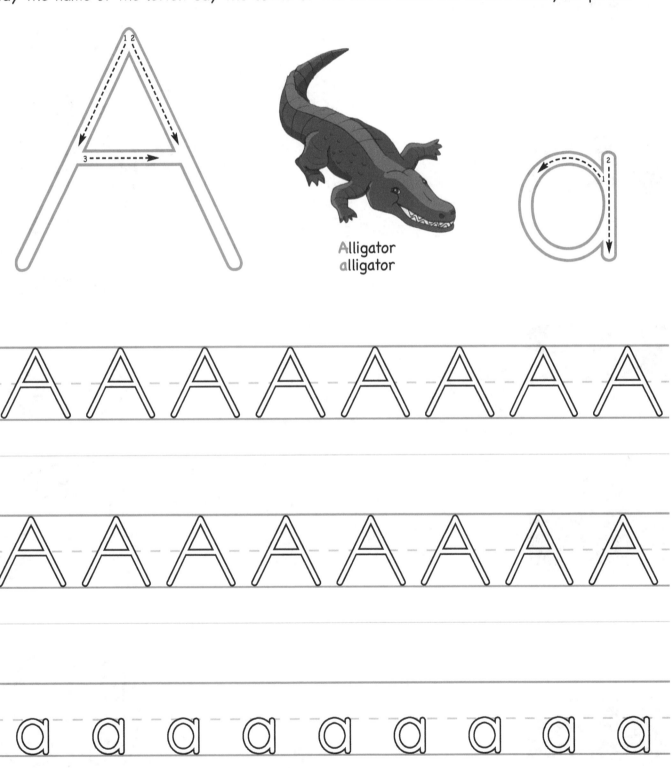

Alligator
alligator

Draw a line to match the clocks that say the same time.

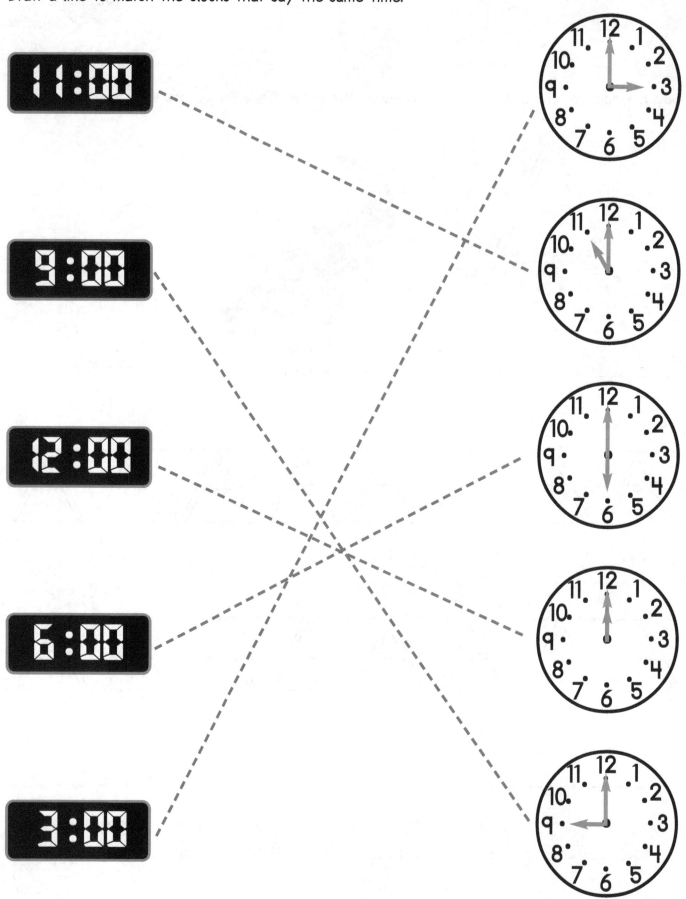

Find the path through the heart maze to help the mother hen find her baby chicks.

Lesson 83 Phonics

Say the name of the letter. Say the sound of the letter. Trace the letters with your pencil.

Antelope
antelope

Trace each shape. Color the circle red. Color the heart yellow. Color the triangle orange.
Color the square blue. Color the rectangle green. You are a star! Color the star your favorite color!

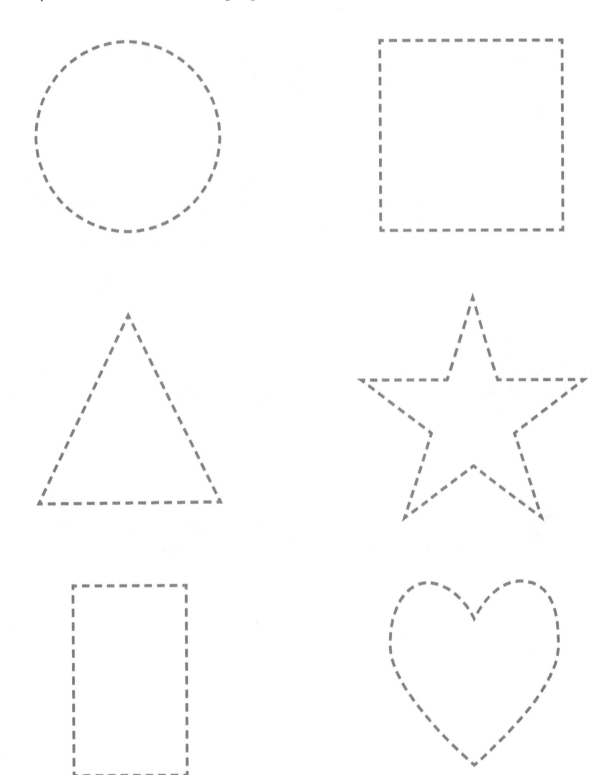

Decorate the memory verse, saying it together with your teacher several times.

I, Jesus, am the bright Morning Star.

Revelation 22:16

Say the name of the letter. Say the sound of the letter. Trace the letters with your pencil.

a a a a a a a a a

Anteater
anteater

337

Draw a line to match the clocks that say the same time.

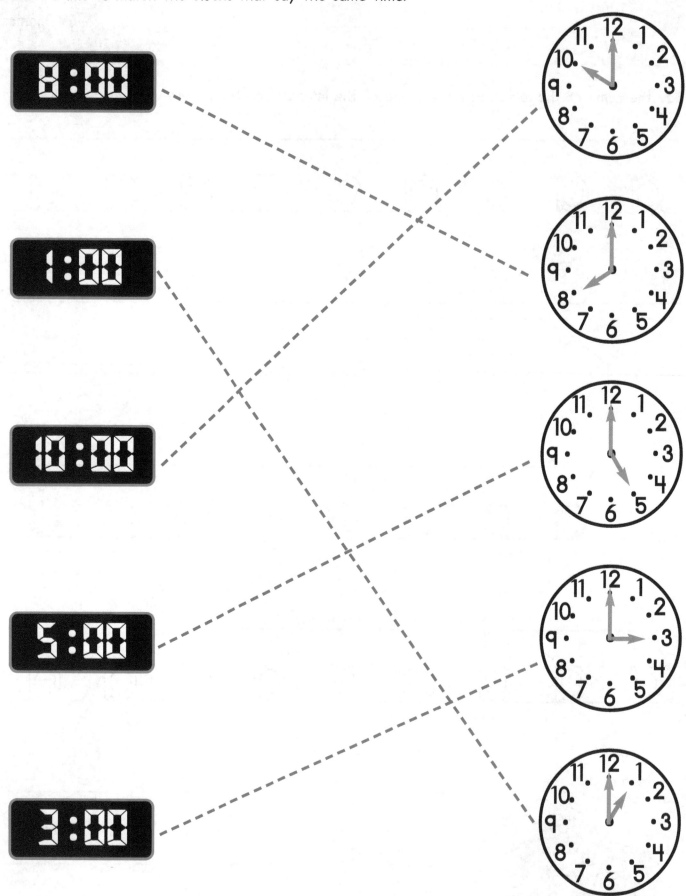

Draw a green circle around the Xx letters, a blue triangle around the Yy letters and
a brown square around the Zz letters.

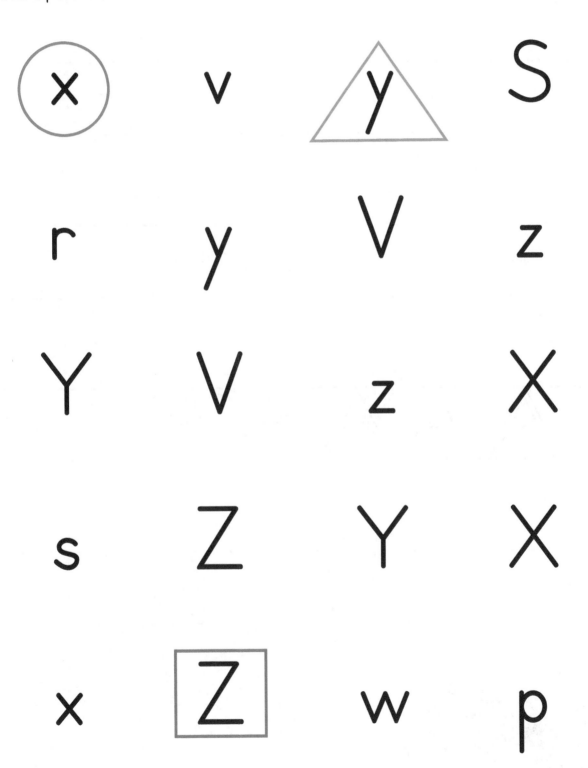

Lesson 85b Phonics

Say the name of the letter. Say the sound of the letter. Trace the letters with your pencil.

Anteater
anteater

Cut out the symbols below and place them on the appropriate day on the calendar that is on
the back of this sheet. The symbols should correspond with activities you would do on the day.

Washing	Playing	Baking	Worship

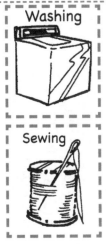   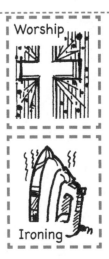

Sewing	Shopping		

Cleaning   Ironing

341

Calendar

Sun	Mon	Tues	Wed	Thur	Fri	Sat
1	2	3	4	5	6	7
8	9	10	11	12	13	14
15	16	17	18	19	20	21
22	23	24	25	26	27	28

Draw a circle around each orange. Draw a rectangle around each banana. Count the apples.

There are _____ apples on the page.

Draw a heart around your favorite fruit.

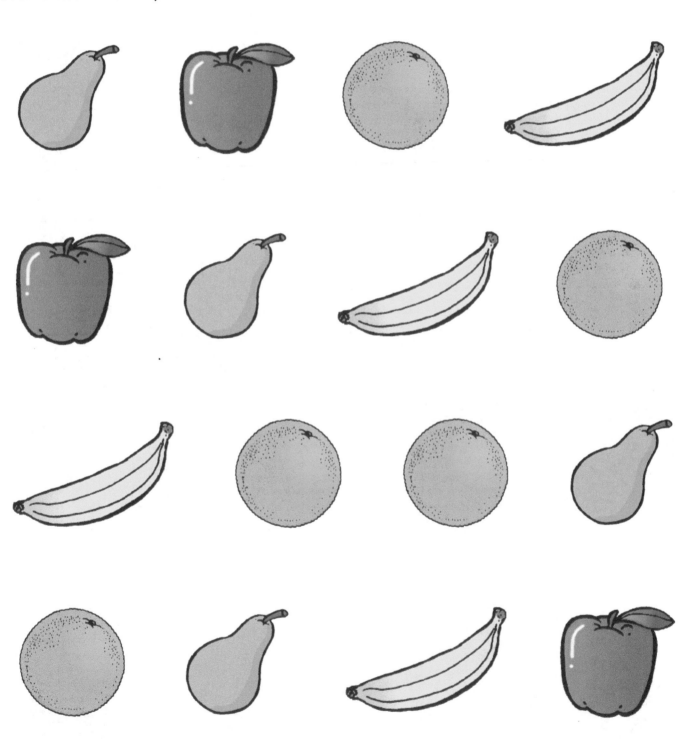

Lesson 86 Writing

Turn this page sideways. Trace each line as closely as you can from the circle to the square.

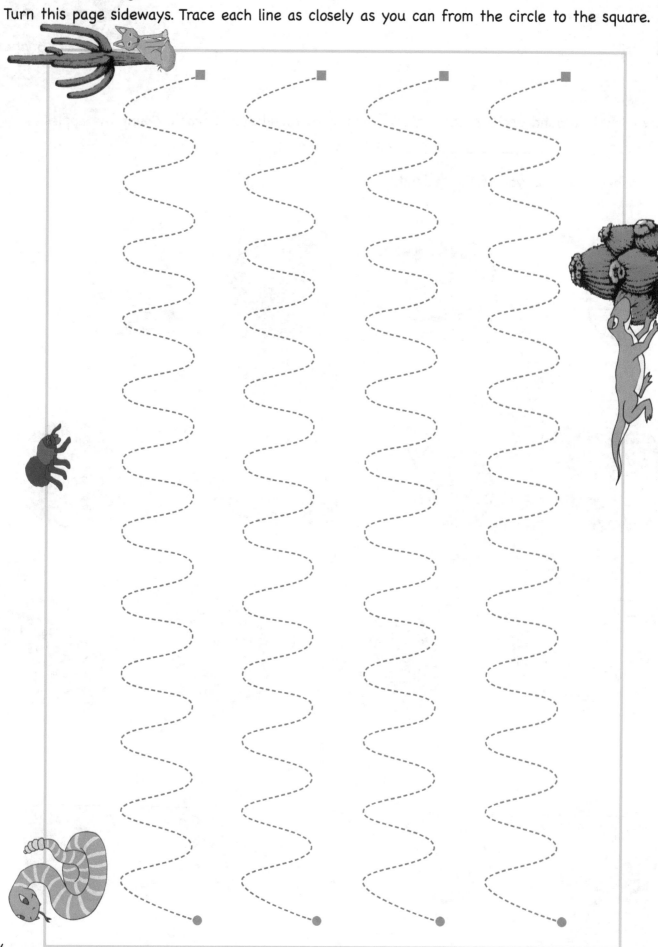

344

Draw a line to match the clocks to the time that they say.

| 4 o'clock |

| 7 o'clock |

| 2 o'clock |

| 5 o'clock |

| 1 o'clock |

345

Count the objects in the box. Trace the numbers on the lines.

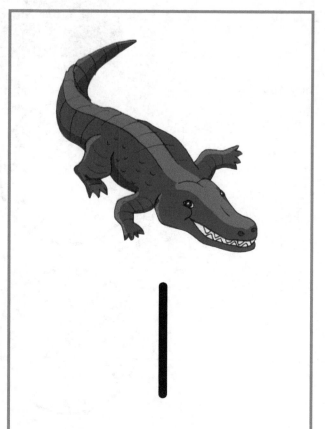

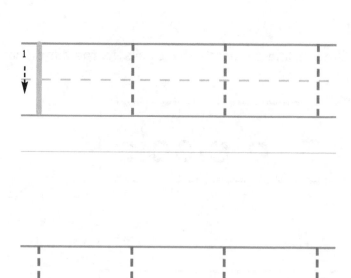

Count the objects in each box. Color the set that shows 1.

Color the bones and cut them out. Save these for counting practice.

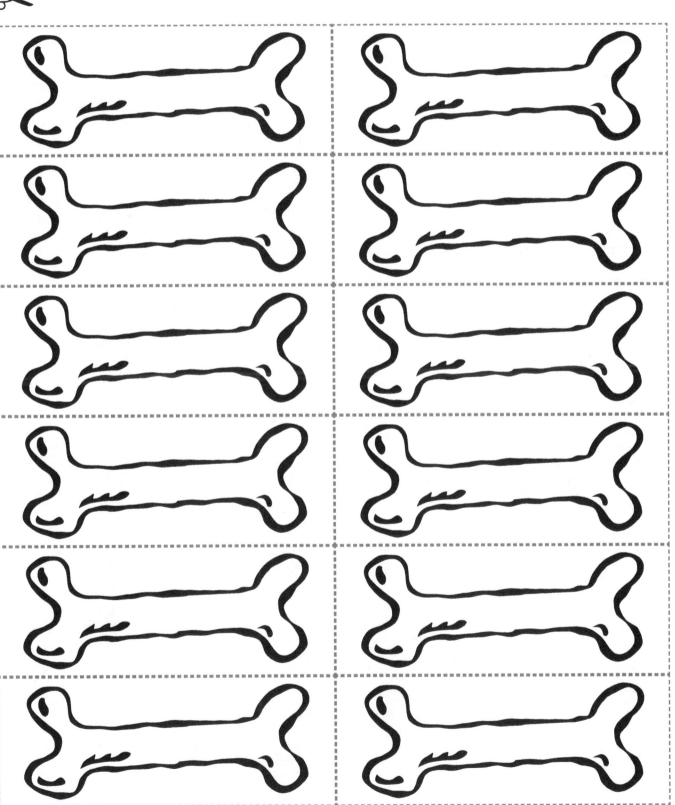

Say the name of the letter. Say the sound of the letter. Trace the letters with your pencil.

Butterfly
butterfly

349

Lesson 87b Phonics

Help the badger get to the ball. Trace the path through the maze to find the ball.

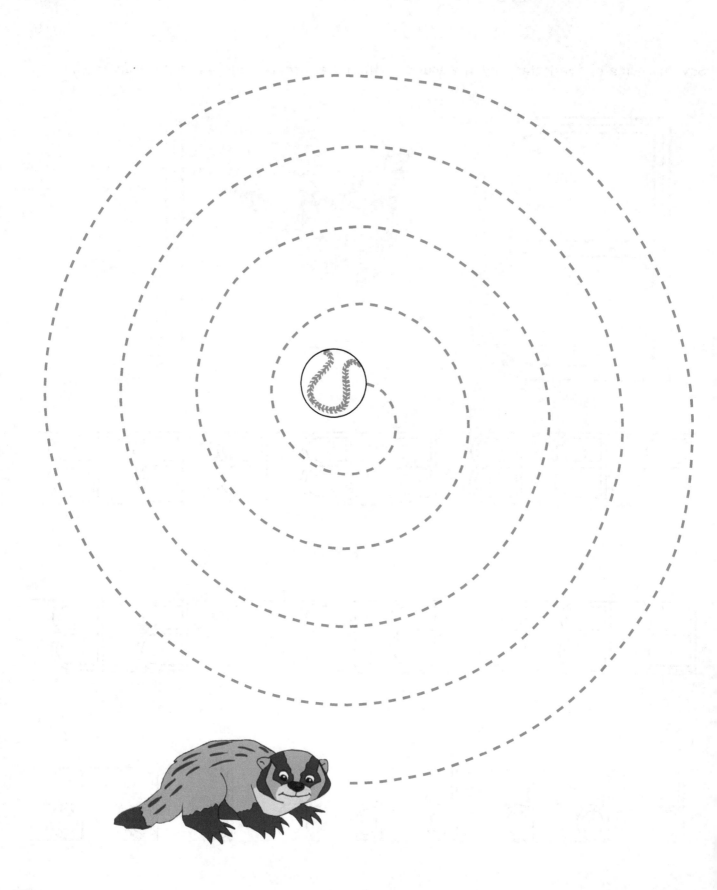

Count the items and say the addition problem. Trace the numbers and say the addition problem again.

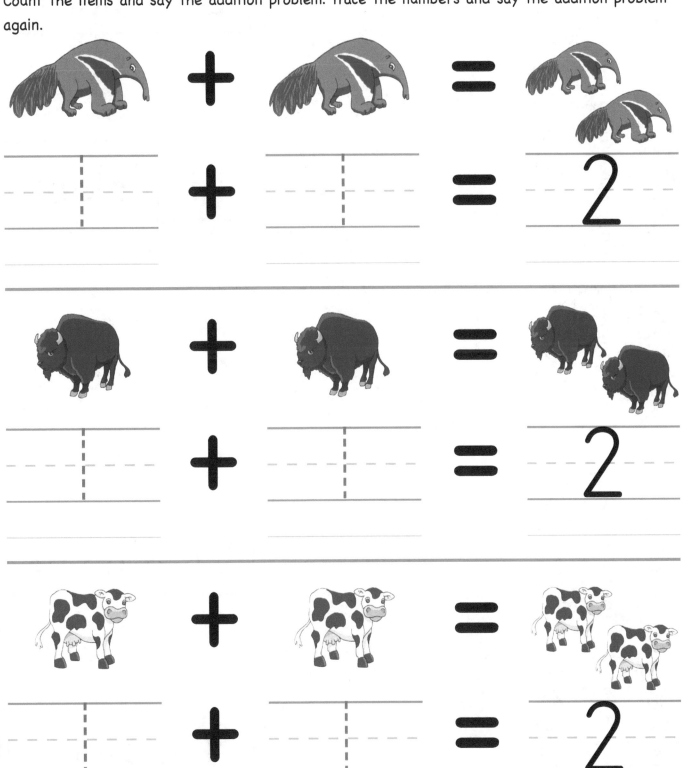

351

Lesson 87b Math

Draw a line to match the clocks to the time that they say.

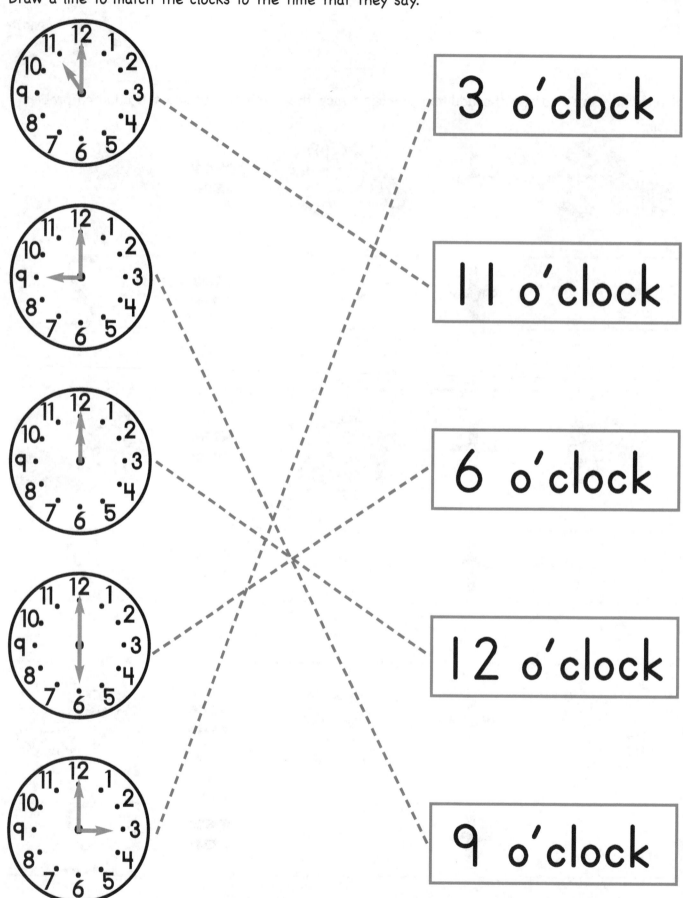

3 o'clock

11 o'clock

6 o'clock

12 o'clock

9 o'clock

Say the name of the letter. Say the sound of the letter. Trace the letters with your pencil.

Bee
bee

Lesson 88 Math

Count the objects in the box. Trace the numbers on the lines.

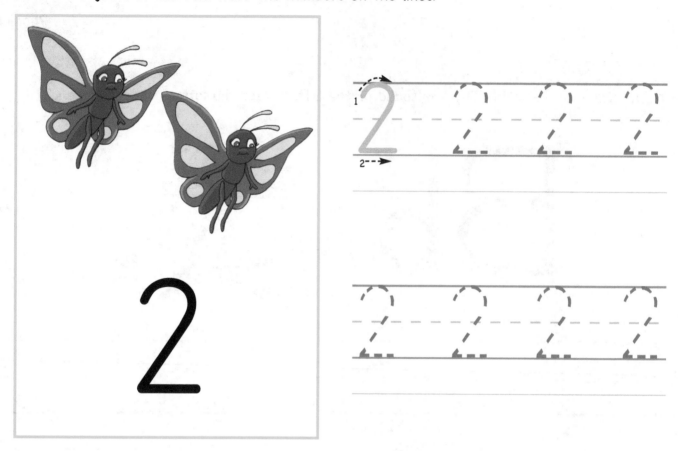

Count the objects in each box. Color the set that shows 2.

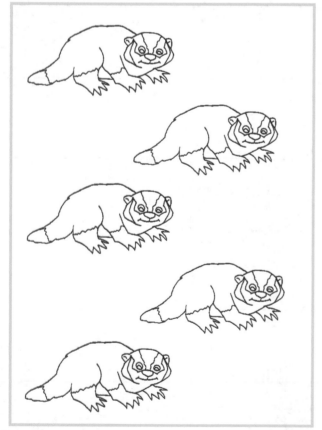

Trace the oval. Trace the letters in the word oval. You may color the oval.

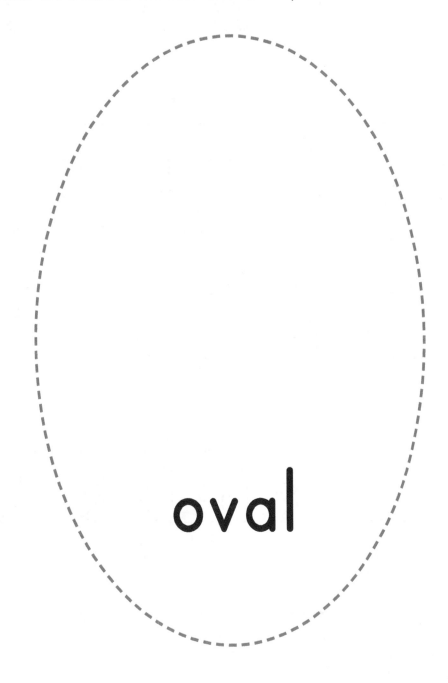

oval

Lesson 89 Phonics

Say the name of the letter. Say the sound of the letter. Trace the letters with your pencil.

Butterfly
butterfly

Count the items and say the addition problem. Trace the numbers and say the addition problem again.

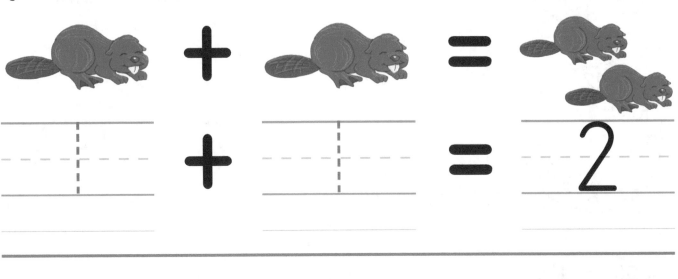

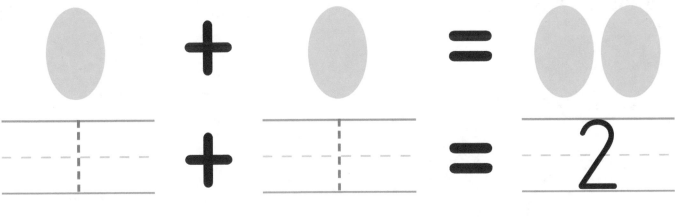

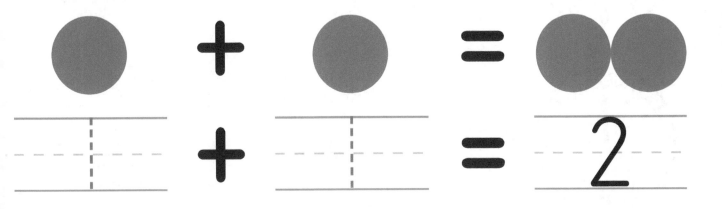

Lesson 89b Math

Draw a line to match the clocks to the time that they say.

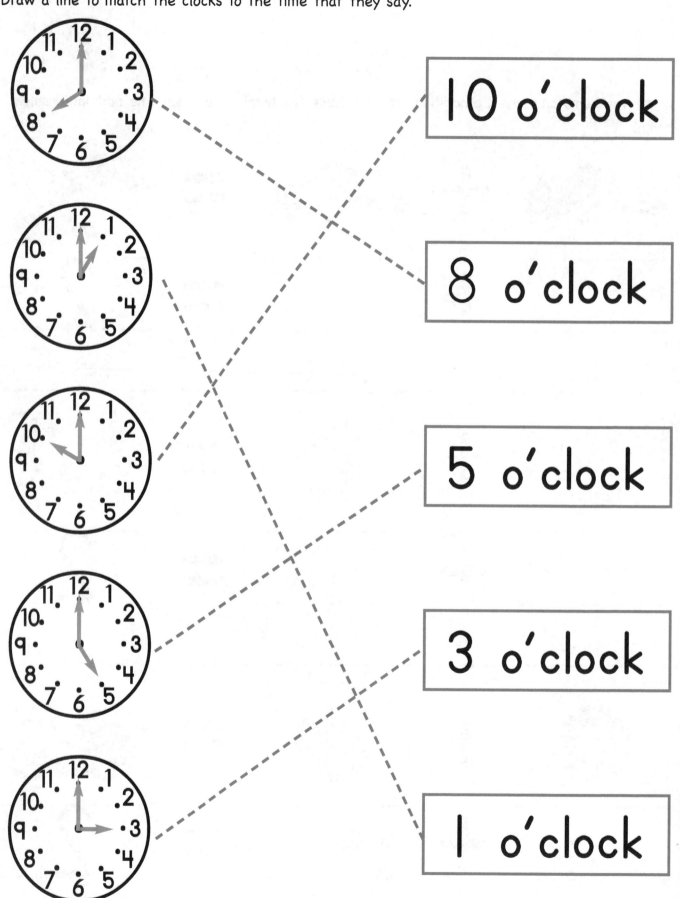

10 o'clock

8 o'clock

5 o'clock

3 o'clock

1 o'clock

Find the path through the butterfly maze.

Lesson 89 Science

The sun, moon, and the planets have symbols. Read the words, trace the symbols with your finger, and trace the dotted symbols with your pencil.

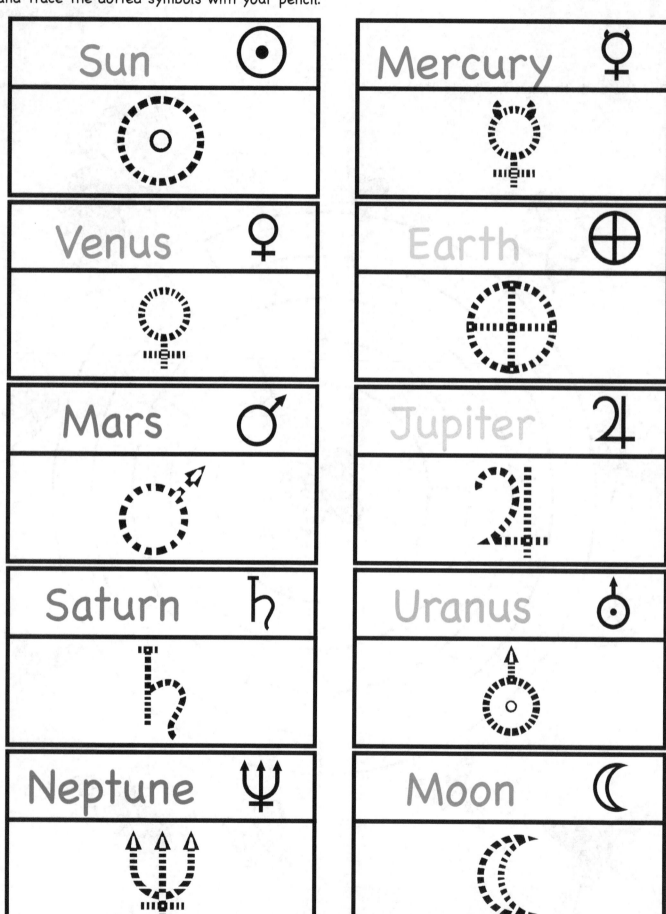

Draw a circle around the Aa–Zz letters and an X on the 0–12 numbers.

4   e   y   a

r   y   8   f

Y   3   z   X

s   Z   G   9

5   d   w   p

Lesson 90b Phonics

Say the name of the letter. Say the sound of the letter. Trace the letters with your pencil.

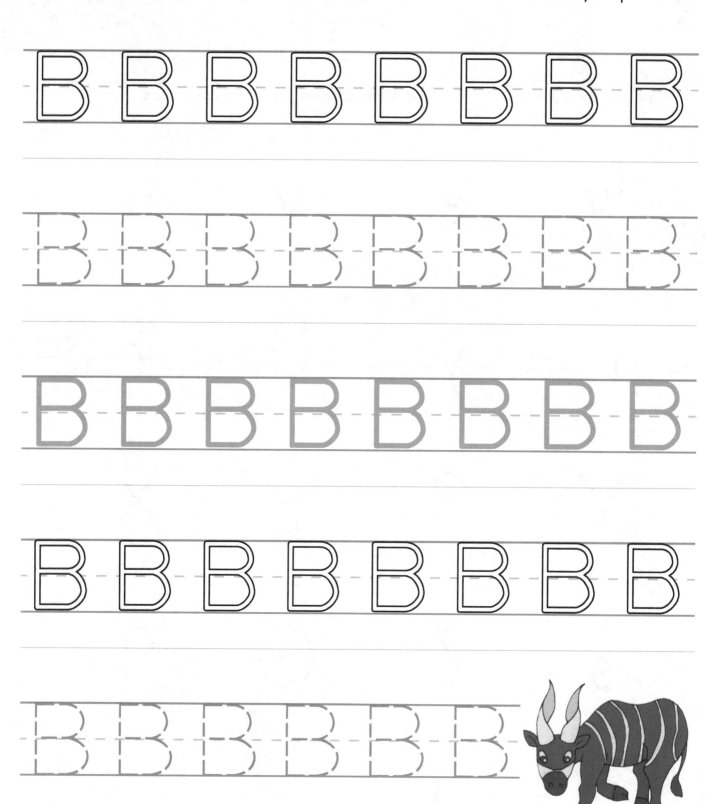

Bongo
bongo

Turn this page sideways. Trace each line as closely as you can from the circle to the square.

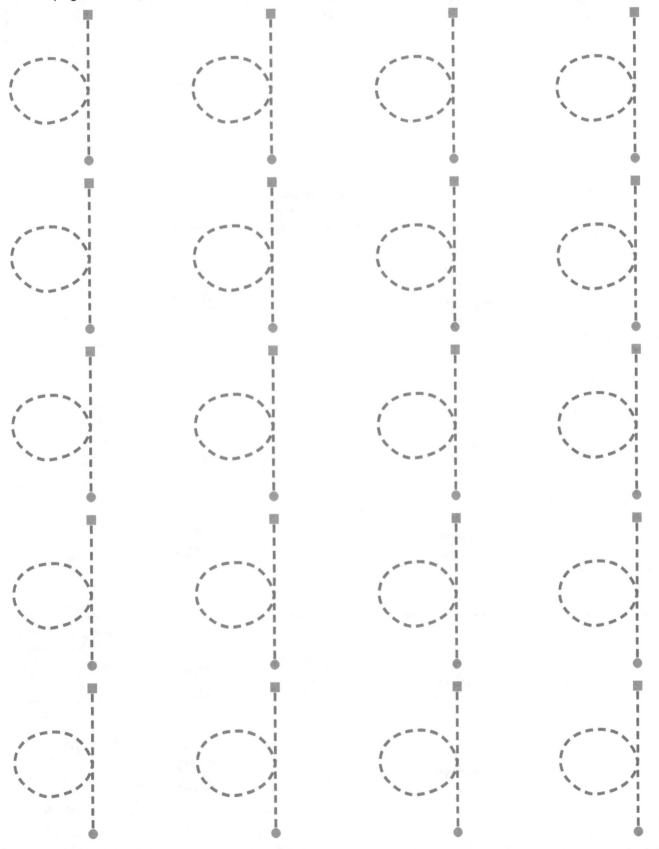

363

Lesson 90a Math

Say the addition problem. Circle the number of items that is the answer. Trace the numbers and say the addition problem again.

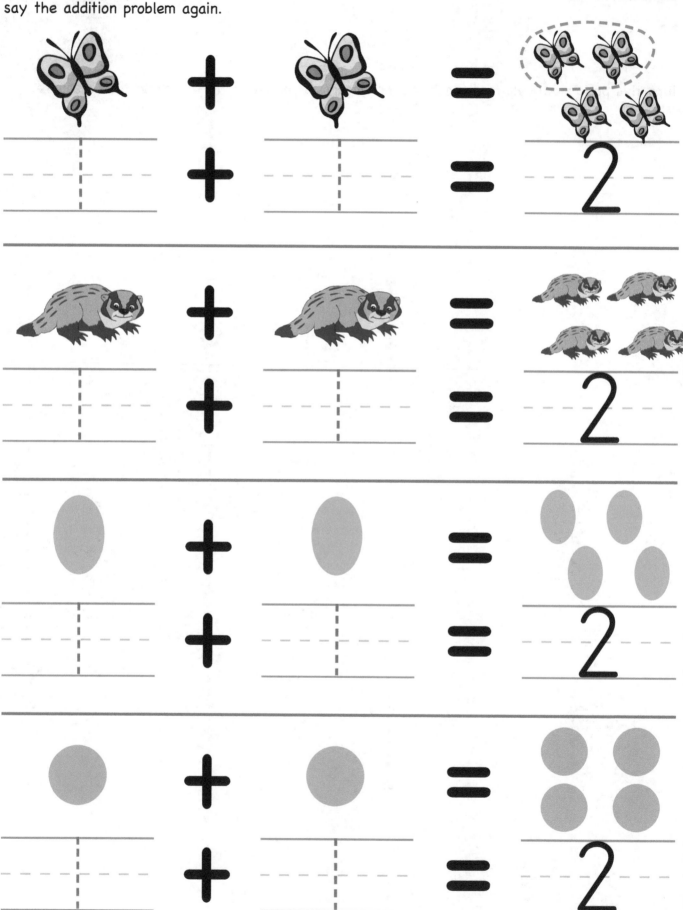

Count the objects in the box. Trace the numbers on the lines.

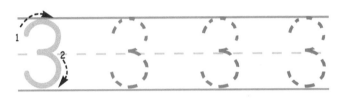

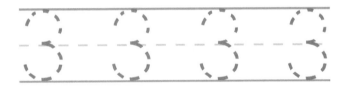

Count the diamonds in each tile. Circle the set that shows 3.